BF

92

Please renew/return this item by the last date shown.

So that your telephone call is charged at local rate, please call the numbers as set out below:

	From Area codes 01923 or 020:	From the rest of Herts:
Renewals:	01923 471373	01438 737373
Enquiries:	01923 471333	01438 737333
Minicom:	01923 471599	01438 737599

L32 www.hertsdirect.org

H.B.B.A.
1982

To John Dony
for showing us the way

Text and maps © Chris Mead and Ken Smith 1982
Illustrations © Kevin Baker 1982

ISBN 0 9507951 0 0

First published in 1982 by H.B.B.A.,
4 Beaconsfield Road, Tring, Hertfordshire HP23 4DP

Phototypeset by Tring Photoset Limited
Printed in England by Maund and Irvine Limited, Tring

CONTENTS

FOREWORD

As all those who took part in the collection of data for this book already know, bird-atlas fieldwork is enormous fun. It takes birdwatchers into remote corners of woodland and fields, along riverbanks and canals, to disused quarries and gravel-pits, and in search of old farm ponds and new plantations: places which might otherwise not be visited by an ornithologist once in a decade. There is always the feeling of breaking new ground and the possibility of making some new and exciting discovery. Even common birds become exciting as a new area is searched for a Goldcrest, a Corn Bunting, a Nightingale, or, perhaps a rookery or even an elusive Coot. This book allows readers to share in this sense of excitement, for all the discoveries made during 1967-73 are clearly mapped, revealing some expected but also many unexpected distributions.

Bird-atlas mapping is carried out within various sizes of grid. On a national scale, the 10 x 10 km square is usual (it was used for *The Atlas of Breeding Birds in Britain and Ireland*); and on the continental scale, Europe will be mapped using 50 x 50 km squares in the forthcoming *Atlas of Breeding Birds in Europe* (fieldwork is planned for 1985-88). For a British county, however, the grid size needs to be finer, and that usually chosen is the 2 x 2 km square (or tetrad) which is used in this Hertfordshire Atlas. These small areas (four square kilometers, or 1½ square miles) are a convenient size for surveying by one or two observers (or a small team) and also give precise detail when mapped, as is demonstrated in this book.

Atlas projects have now been undertaken in the majority of European countries, as well as in Australia, New Zealand and substantial parts of the USA and Canada. The fine-mesh, detailed study by tetrads has, however, been achieved in only a few of the most go-ahead areas of England, where there are not only sufficient observers to carry out the fieldwork but also enthusiastic leaders willing to undertake the administration and organisation. With this book, Hertfordshire joins this elite list of counties (Kent, London and Bedfordshire, with Devon, Huntingdonshire, Lincolnshire and Norfolk soon forthcoming, we hope).

This Atlas reflects many thousands of hours of work, both in the field and at the desk. It provides not only a fascinating picture of bird distributions, with textual explanations of the reasons behind them, and thereby an important conservation document, but also a baseline for future studies. Tomorrow's birdwatchers will, surely, not be able to resist repeating this study to discover the changes which will have occurred as a result of our changing climate and modification to the habitats.

Birdwatchers — present and future, within and outside Hertfordshire — should be grateful to Chris Mead, Ken Smith and their band of helpers for giving us such a valuable and thorough documentation of Hertfordshire's breeding birds in the 1970's.

J. T. R. Sharrock
Blunham, January 1982

Naturalists have always wished to catalogue the animals and plants that they study, not only the differences between varieties but also their distribution. Over the last hundred years books describing the birds of particular areas have been produced for almost everywhere in Britain. However, for the most part, these have simply been based on the intimate local knowledge of the author and the accumulated records in the files of the County Recorder. This book, whilst remaining a part of this long tradition, follows the modern approach by presenting accurate maps of breeding distribution using the objective results of comprehensive fieldwork which covered all parts of the county. Except for a handful of the rarest, each species has its own map with the breeding distribution plotted, dot by dot, using a regular grid of recording areas. Further maps are provided, using the same technique, to show the distribution of various habitat types and physical features through the county.

Hertfordshire has been well served by Bryan Sage's *History of the Birds of Hertfordshire* which was published in 1959. However he was unable to provide detailed distribution maps for, even then, there were too few active bird-watchers in the county to do the necessary fieldwork. It was the botanists who showed the way. In 1962 the Botanical Society of the British Isles published their national *Atlas of the British Flora* using the 10-km squares of the National Grid as the basic recording unit. This was followed, in 1967, by John Dony's *Flora of Hertfordshire* based on the more precise two kilometre squares appropriate for a county survey. Botanists do have certain advantages when it comes to mapping schemes — plants do not fly. However, many ornithologists came to appreciate that this was the future method for gathering distributional data and were soon exploring ways of applying it to birds.

The B.T.O. proposed to survey the summer distribution of breeding birds at the only time of the year when the more mobile species have their interest centred on one place — the nest. A few active birders suggested that the number of birds within each unit should be assessed by the fieldworkers. This was attempted in various different ways during pilot surveys for the National Atlas but the idea was eventually rejected. It was decided, at an early stage, that breeding should be proved beyond doubt wherever possible for each species within each unit surveyed. This system has now been used for the National Atlas in Britain and several other European countries and for many local surveys in Britain. For the country-wide surveys the recording units have been based on whatever suitable maps or map-grids have been available. In Britain and Ireland 10-km squares, in the Netherlands 5-km squares and in France on rectangles 20 km x 27 km: a sensible choice since each unit was precisely covered by a single map. For local surveys the 2 km x 2 km unit is now generally used. Its boundaries are the even numbered kilometre lines of the National Grid: each is thus an area of four square kilometers and is called a *tetrad* from the Greek *tetra* meaning four.

Fieldwork for the Hertfordshire Atlas started in 1967 when, as part of the pilot survey for the National Atlas, the 125 tetrads in the five 10-km squares from Aylesbury (SP81) in the west to Welwyn (TL21) in the east were surveyed by members of the British Trust for Ornithology's staff, Chris Cox, Jim Flegg and Tom Gladwin. The results were encouraging but the proposition that tetrads should be used for the National Atlas was rejected. However, it was thought that there were sufficient observers in Hertfordshire for the whole county to be covered at the tetrad level. Thus, from 1968, the criteria used nationally for recording on the 10-km square unit were used in Hertfordshire at the tetrad level: the combined records from its constituent 25 tetrads forming a complete 10-km square record for the National Atlas. Any species recorded in the breeding season in possible breeding habitat, that is, for example, ignoring loafing non-breeding gulls, could be entered into the Atlas records in one of three ways:

Possibly breeding   *Column 1 record*

Entry in first column on the recording card.
A species seen in possible breeding habitat during its breeding season.
No further indication that it might actually be breeding.

Probably breeding   *Column 2 record*

Entry in second column on card.
Species seen in likely breeding habitat and suspected to be breeding.
Criteria included birds holding territory, persistently singing etc.

Proved breeding   *Column 3 record*

Entry in third column on the card.
Species definitely breeding — nest and egg or young found, parents feeding newly fledged young etc.

Each entry had a code — column one a simple tick, column two a single letter indicating the sort of evidence found and column three a double letter code, again indicating the evidence found. Effectively as soon as a species was proved to breed in a tetrad further records of it could be ignored.

The recording card used in Hertfordshire was very similar to that used for the national survey but, of course, showed a more restricted species list. It also asked for rather more information on coverage and, for a minority of species, an estimate of the number of breeding pairs within the tetrad.

The majority of observers were recruited from the B.T.O. membership within the county and from the ranks of the Hertfordshire Natural History Society. In addition records were received through the Royal Society for the Protection of Birds, the *Farmer's Weekly* (particularly useful for Barn Owls), schools, local newspapers and even via Radio One after Tim Sharrock, the national organiser, had made a series of midnight appearances! In some areas, for example near Bishop's Stortford and round Stevenage, active local societies provided excellent coverage through their members. As many helpers as possible are acknowledged in the back of this Atlas (page 124) — we are grateful to them all and especially any we have omitted.

Although the National Atlas fieldwork was to run from 1968 to 1972 we decided to include the 1967 tetrad survey data in the local Atlas. Each year assessments were made as to how well the local coverage was progressing. By 1971 it was clear that there were few, if any, areas where new records for 10-km squares would be obtained but that there were quite a number of tetrads which were poorly covered. Some of these gaps were plugged in 1972 but we decided to make a special effort during 1973, after the National Atlas had finished. By the end of summer 1973 only two tetrads with any part of Hertfordshire in them had not been surveyed. In both cases minute parts of the county were involved and both tetrads have been completely excluded from the survey, they were TQ09 A and TL30 Y. Otherwise all tetrads with any part of Hertfordshire in them have been included and, to allow for a reasonable comparison, the whole of every tetrad was surveyed rather than what may be only a small part within the county. Also to make the Atlas as complete as possible we have taken our definition of Hertfordshire to include any area which has been part of the administrative county of Hertfordshire since 1859, when the Watsonian vice-county system was devised (Hertfordshire is v.c. 20).

The fieldwork was great fun. It appealed to the more or less suppressed collecting instinct within every observer, for one only had to move to the next tetrad for even the humble House Sparrow to become a new record. It was a challenge to the skilled ornithologists who took part and considered it a matter of some pride to prove as many species as possible rather than to have them on the card as lowly ticks. Many felt that their fieldcraft had gained tremendously from taking part.Finally it appealed to everyone as an obviously objective means of recording the county's breeding bird distribution.

Observers were encouraged to visit the tetrads for which they were responsible several times from March through to July. Some species, such as Mistle Thrush, are much easier to record early in the season whilst others, like Corn Buntings, are easier later. Direct disturbance of breeding birds was discouraged for proving breeding through observations of parents feeding newly fledged young is much easier and safer for the birds than actual nest-finding. There were few tetrads for which we did not receive several cards. Sometimes these came from the same observer in different years but, in most cases, several observers were involved.

Many observers were, of course, submitting records for their home area where many of the birds they were recording could really be counted as old friends. However even they often discovered areas within a short walk of home that they never knew existed and certainly birds which they did not believe bred so close. The instructions to Atlas workers relied crucially on the incomparable maps of the Ordnance Survey. Not only did they show the grid lines and therefore the boundaries of the tetrads and the reference numbers of the 10-km squares but also they showed the local area. The 1 : 25 000 series (2½" : 1 mile) are in sufficient detail to show every building, field boundary, wood, copse, path and pond. The Atlas worker confronted with a strange tetrad would ideally look at this map and decide to visit the main stretches of water, woods etc. In recent years many towns and villages have spread very quickly swallowing what was countryside. Their spread, in certain parts of the county has also caused extensive gravel diggings which, in their turn, provide particularly good habitats for birds. Coverage within the county was so good that we think all such areas will have been found and recorded.

The completed cards were destined for CJM's card index in Tring however, for much of the county during the final stages of the survey, they were first sent to organisers covering particular 10-km squares. These organisers, with an intimate knowledge of their own patch, were in a very good position to make immediate

7

checks for mis-identifications and mis-readings of maps resulting in the incorrect use of tetrad letters. We would particularly like to thank Brian Barton, Mike Barrett, Tim Beynon, Richard Blindell, Jack Dowsett, Joy Franklin, Tom Gladwin, Stewart Linsell, Tony Prater, Roy Sanderson, Brian Sawford and Peter Walton who undertook these checks. Final checks were made when the cards reached Tring and later when the maps were plotted. At this stage additional information from the County Recorder's files was incorporated. Hertfordshire workers were responsible for all the county's tetrads within the London Natural History Society area and information was freely exchanged between us and with the Bedfordshire Natural History Society for their Atlas. The slight differences between our maps and theirs and the 10-km maps of the National Atlas mostly relate to the slight differences in time-scale of fieldwork.

The Hertfordshire Breeding Bird Atlas also contains information about the habitats available to the birds. Just as we have been able to present the bird distribution data in an objective form so also the habitat information is presented as dot maps. Many rely heavily on the Land Utilisation Survey maps of Hertfordshire held at King's College London. The survey had been completed in years when our fieldwork was starting and provided the ideal supplement to the basic 1:25 000 Ordnance Survey map data. We intend to use this for a much more detailed survey of the habitat requirements of the breeding birds of Hertfordshire than would be appropriate in this book.

Changes have undoubtedly taken place since the fieldwork was finished in 1973. To try to assess how these may have affected the commoner species we have also undertaken an analysis of the local data held by the British Trust for Ornithology from the Common Birds Census. This survey assesses the population change in breeding birds from year to year by mapping the territory-holding birds on a plot in successive years. Since rather few plots actually fall within Hertfordshire we used them and any in the adjacent counties (Greater London, Buckinghamshire, Bedfordshire, Cambridgeshire and Essex) which were within 40 kilometres of Hertfordshire. In the best years some 35 or 40 plots were available for comparison, holding on average, about 200 pairs each of the more common species we have analysed. For some species the C.B.C. figures are only mentioned but, for many, the local and national indices are plotted. The local index, being based on fewer plots sometimes shows a different slope from the national data but such discrepancies are often due to the small local samples available in 1966 — the year on which most indices are based. We have plotted all the indices on a log scale for there were several species which have undergone large-scale changes during the period since the C.B.C. started in 1962.

We have also taken the opportunity to publish a brief but complete list of the birds recorded in the county. This is based on Bryan Sage's work over many years and supplemented by the records published in the County Bird Report. The continuing co-operation of all bird-watchers in the county is sought, throughout the year, in the submission of records to the County Recorder, currently Bruce Taggart (see page 127).

Hertfordshire is a medium sized county situated immediately north of Greater London and adjacent to Buckinghamshire, Bedfordshire, Cambridgeshire and Essex. Figure 2.1 is a map of the county showing the major towns and railway routes. The present county boundary is shown by the heavy line whilst the dotted ones show boundaries in use at some time between 1859 and 1965. The latest changes, part of the extensive re-organisation of English and Welsh administrative areas, resulted in the loss of Barnet and the acquisition of Potters Bar. At the same time there were minor adjustments in the Luton area and along the northern edge of the county. The present area of 163 415 hectares is very slightly less than the pre-1965 figure of 163 706 hectares. The main centres of population are concentrated in the south of the county and along the major communication routes. In 1981 the population was 954 535 giving twice the average density for the whole of the United Kingdom. The position of the county, close to London and astride several major national communication routes has led to very heavy development pressures. The well established market towns have grown significantly in recent decades and major new town developments have taken place at Hemel Hempstead, Hatfield, Welwyn Garden City, Stevenage and Letchworth. The network of suburban railway routes and, in the south, the northern extension of underground services allow commuters to offices in central London to live almost anywhere over large parts of the county.

Fifty years ago the human population of the county was only about 400 000. With 30 years growth at an annual rate of more than 1.7% this had risen to 790 000 in 1961. Since then the growth rate has been rather less than 1%. Over the same fifty year period the amount of land in urban use rose more slowly from 16 000 to 34 000 hectares. The extensive road building operations of the past two or three decades have also taken their toll. There are now more than 60 kilometres of motorway in the county using over 500 hectares and many other roads have been widened to accommodate the ever increasing demands of road transport. In 1931 some 125 000 hectares were farmed in the county — over three quarters of the total area. By 1980 this total had fallen to 105 000 hectares, rather less than two thirds of the total area and a decrease of 16%. However, despite these developments, Hertfordshire is still predominantly a rural and agricultural county. Away from the main centres of population, particularly in the northeast, there are wide tracts of rolling countryside with the occasional copse or small wood and hardly a village or hamlet to be seen.

Hertfordshire lies on the northern rim of the London Basin. The chalks hills of the Chilterns and their eastern extension run along the northern border from Tring to Royston with the highest point just west of Hastoe, near Tring at 245 m.a.s.l. (804 feet). The relief of the county is shown in figure 2.2. Although there are several gaps in these hills the two main ones are the Tring gap, used by the Grand Union Canal and by the main railway route from Euston, and the Hitchin gap which has the main east coast railway route to Scotland from King's Cross. The northern edge of the chalk hills forms a prominent escarpment in the west overlooking the clay vales of Buckinghamshire and Bedfordshire. To the east the hills are not so high and generally form a lower, less marked scarp slope. The dip slope of the chalk falls to the southeast to the major river valleys of central Hertfordshire — the Lea and the Colne. Beyond these valleys the land rises again

2.1 MAJOR TOWNS AND RAILWAYS

This outline map of Hertfordshire shows the position and extent of the major built-up areas at the time of the Atlas. The dark lines show the British Rail routes in the county. Most of the railways are over a century old and the urban developments have clearly concentrated along them. The sparsely populated northeast corner of the county is not served by a railway.

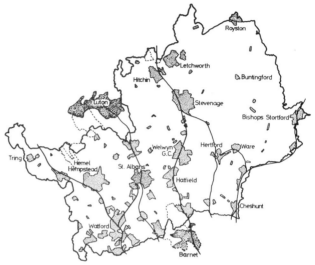

to the South Hertfordshire plateau. The lowest point in the county is 15 m.a.s.l. (55 feet) near Cheshunt where the River Lea flows into Greater London.

The majority of Hertfordshire is in the Thames catchment. Figure 2.3 shows the main rivers, the Lea and the Colne, and their tributaries. The Colne appears near Hatfield and flows through Watford and Rickmansworth leaving the county eventually to join the Thames at Staines. Its major tributaries in Hertfordshire are the Ver, the Gade and the Chess. The River Lea rises in Bedfordshire just north of Luton and flows through Harpenden, Wheathampstead, Welwyn Garden City, Hertford and Ware. There it is joined by the Stort and turns south to Cheshunt and reaches the Thames just east of the Isle of Dogs. Its major tributaries within the county are the Mimram, Beane, Rib, Ash and Stort. Parts of the northern

2.2 ALTITUDE

Land more than 151 m (500′) above sea level

Land above 106 m (350′)

Land above 46 m (150′)

Other areas (blank) are lower than this. They are only in the Colne and Lea valleys and the area north of Baldock.

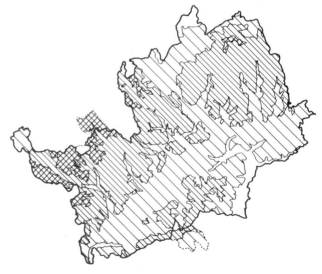

10

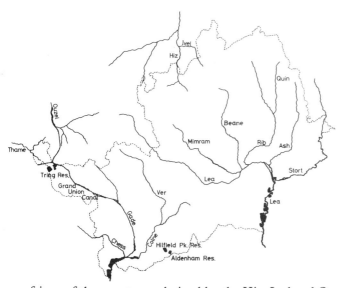

2.3 RIVERS, CANALS AND LAKES

On this map the county boundary is shown dotted so that rivers running along it may be distinguished. The hatched lines show canals and the solid areas indicate large stretches of open water. Minor streams and tributaries are not marked on this map (but see figure 3.7).

fringe of the county are drained by the Hiz, Ivel and Ouzel into the Great Ouse which flows into the Wash. North of Tring in the Vale of Aylesbury, the drainage is into the Thame and thence the Thames. The two major artificial waterways are the Grand Union Canal, which follows the line of the Colne, Gade and Bulborne to leave the county just northeast of Tring, and the Lea and Stort Navigations, which follow the Lea and the Stort to Ware and Bishop's Stortford respectively. Figure 2.3 also shows the major areas of open water. Most of these are the extensive disused gravel workings in the Lea and Colne valleys but there are also the canal water supply reservoirs at Tring and Aldenham and the drinking water reservoir at Hilfield Park.

The underlying solid geology of Hertfordshire is very simple with the Chalk beds, laid down about a 100 million years ago on the bottom of a shallow area of sea during the Cretaceous period, sloping down to the southeast. To the north these form the scarp of the Chilterns and the northern rim of the London Basin. They dip downwards and extend under London to reappear in Surrey as the North Downs. In the south of the county the Eocene deposits of the London Clay, Reading Beds and Pebble Gravels overlay the Chalk. This layering is shown in section, from northwest to southeast, in figure 2.4.

However this simple solid geology is hidden by the very complex surface deposits resulting from the more recent glaciations. Figure 2.5 is a necessarily much simplified map of the surface geology. Only on the high ground and along the valley edges does the Chalk reach the surface. Elsewhere it is overlain by Clay-

2.4 GEOLOGICAL SECTION This section through the county, from northwest to southeast, shows the Chalk beneath the more recent Reading Beds and London Clay. The vertical scale is greatly exaggerated.

11

2.5 SUPERFICIAL GEOLOGY

Gault Clay

Chalk

Clay-with- flints

Boulder Clay

Valley Gravels

London Clay

Alluvium

Complex deposits, particularly in the London Clay area, have been greatly simplified.

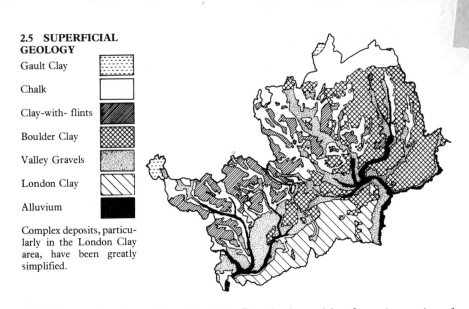

with-flints or, in the northeast, Boulder Clay: both resulting from the erosion of the overlaid Eocene deposits. In the river valleys there are extensive gravel beds and terraces which are the basis for the economically (and ornithologically) important extractive industries. On the South Hertfordshire Plateau the local surface geology is much too complicated to show in detail on the map. John Dony in his *Flora of Hertfordshire* divided the surface geology of the county into six broad regions: the Chalk, Boulder Clay, Clay-with-flints, Lea Gravels, Colne Gravels and London Clay. These are shown on figure 2.6 with a seventh — the Gault Clay just north of Tring and north of Ashwell where it emerges from beneath the Chalk. The surface geology is a major influence on the habitats available for birds within the county.

2.6 GEOLOGICAL REGIONS

This simple map was used by John Dony, in his *Flora*, to demonstrate the overall effect of the surface geology on plant communities in the county. Each region has its own definite characteristics but there are, of course, areas within each that do not conform to the overall pattern. The plant communities of these regions largely determine the avifauna found in the county.

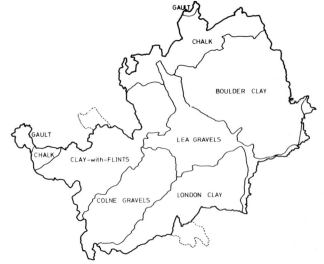

HERTFORDSHIRE BREEDING BIRD ATLAS

Geological Regions

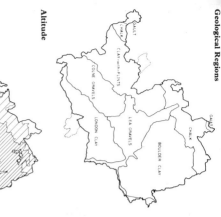

Altitude

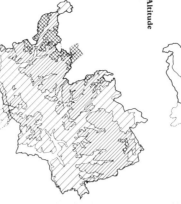

Urban Areas

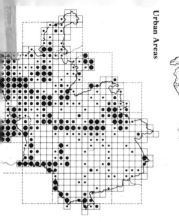

Superficial Geology

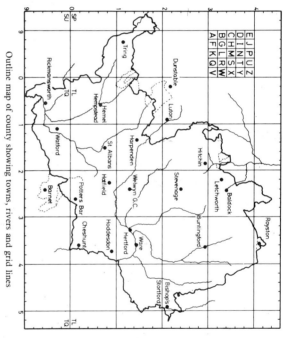

Outline map of county showing towns, rivers and grid lines

Extractive Industry

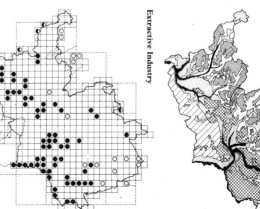

Quality of Coverage

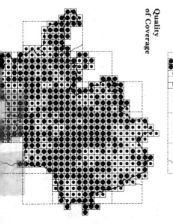

Geological Regions – after Dony

Altitude ⊠ Above 151 m ▨ 106-151 m
▢ 46-106 m ▢ Blank – below 46 m

Urban Areas – the developed area of each tetrad
● More than 30%   ● 15-30%   • 3-15%
Blank – less than 3%

Superficial Geology –
▢ Chalk   ⊠ Gault Clay
▨ Clay-with-flints   ▨ Valley Gravels
⊠ Boulder Clay   ■ Alluvium
▢ London Clay

Extractive Industry in each tetrad
○ Chalk   ● Clay   ● Sand and/or gravel

Quality of Coverage – number of species recorded as % of assessment
● 80% or more   ● 50-79%   ● 40-49%

Grassland

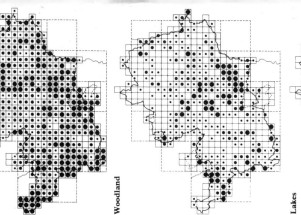

Woodland

Lakes

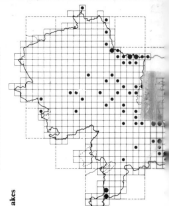

HERTFORDSHIRE BREEDING BIRD ATLAS

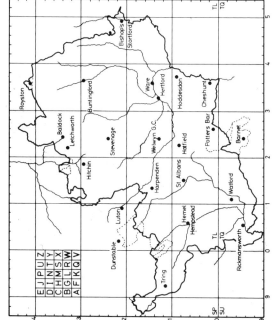

An outline map of the county showing the major towns and rivers and the National Grid squares.

Arable Farmland – the area of each tetrad devoted to arable
● More than 30% ● 15-30% • 3-15%
Blank – less than 3%

Semi-natural Woodland – the area in each tetrad
● More than 20% ● 10-20% • 3-10%
Blank – less than 3%

Rivers and Streams – the largest watercourse in each tetrad
● River or canal • Stream • Brook

Grassland – area of grassland in each tetrad
● More than 30% ● 15-30% • 3-15%
Blank – less than 3%

Woodland – the total area of woodland in each tetrad
● More than 20% ● 10-20% • 3-10%
Blank – less than 3%

Lakes – the area of open water in each tetrad
● More than 20 hectares
• Less than 20 hectares

Arable Farmland

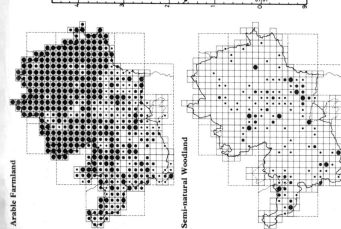

Semi-natural Woodland

Rivers and Streams

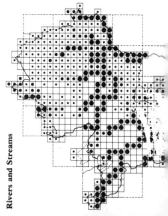

The distribution of breeding birds in an area will largely depend on its physical features and vegetation, which, in their turn, depend on the geology, soil type and climate. However by far the most important influence in Hertfordshire is provided by man's activities. All the habitats over the whole county are only there as a result of man's efforts. Even the few areas of ancient woodland have been managed by man for centuries. Their very special natural history and conservation interest is preserved through this continuity which, in many cases, has allowed them to retain aspects of the flora and fauna of the primeval forests. Many other habitats of high natural history value depend upon man's management for their continued interest. Examples are provided by the chalk grasslands which are dependant on sheep grazing and the rapidly disappearing herb-rich meadows dependant on annual grazing and cropping for hay. However, much as we would like to see more of these 'Blue Ribbon' habitats, which provide sanctuary for the locally rare species, it is the ordinary areas of farmland, rivers, gravel pits and woodland which are most important for the commoner birds. The maps in this section depict the distribution of these habitats. The sources consulted included the 1:25 000 Ordnance Survey Maps, the Second Land Utilisation Survey (1963-1968), which are lodged at King's College, London and the Hertfordshire and Middlesex Trust for Nature Conservation's survey of ancient woodlands.

Although the area of land in Hertfordshire devoted to agriculture has been steadily decreasing it still amounts to 64.3% of the area of the county. The huge changes in agricultural practice have therefore had an enormous effect on Hertfordshire bird habitats over the last 50-100 years. In the 1930's about half the agricultural land was down to permanent grass. During the Second World War very large tracts were ploughed up to increase the home production of food and most has remained in use as arable. In 1962 the area down to permanent grass had fallen to 27% and the decline has continued. This loss of pasture has been accompanied by a fall in the sheep population from 170 000 eighty years ago to about 40 000 now. In the same period cattle numbers have increased from 34 000 to 60 000. Surprisingly the 12 000 working horses on farms recorded at the turn of the century are probably now out-numbered by horses and ponies kept for riding. The crops grown on the arable have also changed with roots dropping to a third the area with the decline in the sheep population. The cereals now grown include very few oats but much more barley, formerly less than a fifth and now three or four times this amount.

The distribution of arable land at the start of the Atlas period, derived from the Land Utilisation Survey 1963-1968, is shown in figure 3.1. It is clear that the major arable areas are on the Boulder Clay, Chalk and, to a lesser extent, the Clay-with-flints. In fact some tetrads in the northeast of the county were over 80% arable. In the urban south arable is almost completely absent. The distribution of grassland shown in figure 3.2 indicates a clear concentration in the south on the acidic clay soils. There are also a few pockets in the river valleys of the northeast and a major area on the Gault Clay of the Vale of Aylesbury northwest of Tring. Of course in many suburban areas any agricultural land is likely to be put down to grass for horses.

3.1 ARABLE FARM-LAND

This map shows the distribution, tetrad by tetrad,of arable farmland within Hertfordshire. The percentage area of each tetrad devoted to arable is shown by the size of dot:

- ●   More than 30%
- •   15% — 30%
- ·   3% — 15%

Blank tetrads have less than 3% arable, many of these are in the urbanised south of the county.

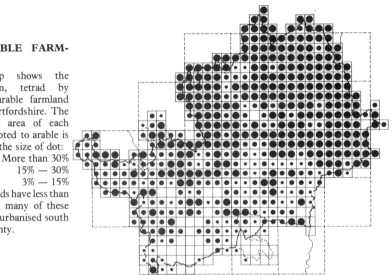

After the last Ice Age and before the arrival of man the climax vegetation of the whole of the county would have been forest. However, even by Norman times (900 years ago), approximately two thirds had been cleared. For most of the twentieth century about 6½% of the county has been wooded: mostly in areas with poor soils. This is a low percentage cover compared with Kent (10%) and Sussex (14%) but higher than Bedfordshire (4%). The distribution of major areas of woodland is shown in figure 3.3. This includes all woodland types: natural, semi-natural and planted, coniferous, deciduous and mixed. The major woods in the west are centred on the Ashridge Estate but the county's main woodlands are on

3.2 GRASSLAND

In this map the area of grassland within each tetrad is represented by the size of dot (as in 3.1):

- ●   More than 30%
- •   15% — 30%
- ·   3% — 15%

Blank tetrads have less than 3% grassland. In the developed south of the county much of the available farmland is down to grass.

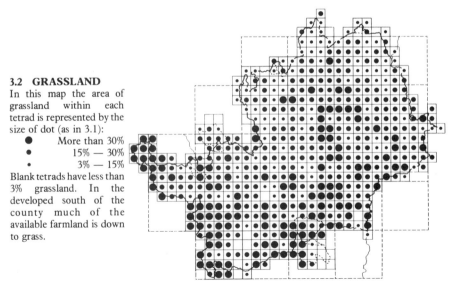

14

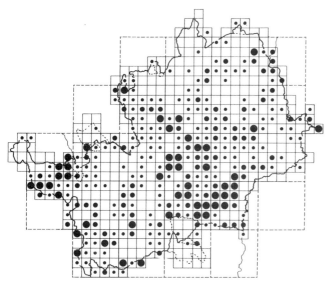

3.3 WOODLAND

The area of woodland in each tetrad is represented by the size of dot:

●   More than 20%
●   10% — 20%
•   3% — 10%

Blank tetrads contained less than 3% of woodland. All sorts of woodlands were included but no allowance was made for hedgerow or garden trees or for orchards. Of the 47 tetrads with more than 20% woodland only four (two in SP91 and two in TL30) were more than 50% wooded.

the London Clay in TL20 and TL30. These include Northaw Great Wood, Hatfield Park, Derry's Wood, Wormley Wood, Bencroft Wood, Broxbourne, Cowheath and Highfield Woods and also Box Wood. There is another concentration between Welwyn Garden City and Stevenage which includes Sherrardspark Wood, Bramfield Forest, Hitch Wood and the Knebworth complex.

The main change in the woodlands over the last 40 years has been the felling of deciduous trees and the planting of coniferous species. The distribution of the remaining areas of semi-natural woodland, mainly derived from the County

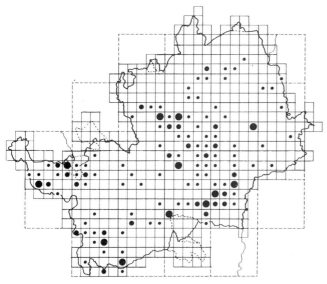

3.4 SEMI-NATURAL WOODLAND

This map shows the area of semi-natural woodland in each tetrad, using the same codes as figure 3.3:

●   More than 20%
●   10% — 20%
•   3% — 10%

Blank tetrads had less than 3% semi-natural woodland by area. Only three tetrads had over 100 hectares: TL12 W, TL20 X and TL30 P.

3.5 DEVELOPED AREAS

This map shows the percentage of each tetrad covered by urban, suburban or industrial development:

● More than 30%

● 15% — 30%

• 3% — 15%

Blank tetrads may contain one or two farms or a small hamlet but no more extensive developments. Areas devoted to railway and road routes are not included.

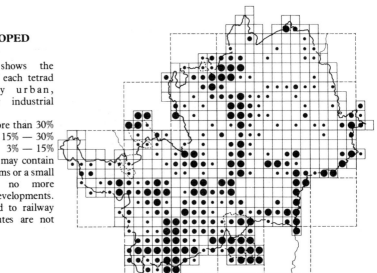

Trust's recent survey, is shown in figure 3.4. Some 4000 hectares of the county's 10 500 hectares of woodland are still 'semi-natural'. Their species composition is generally well correlated with the local soil type. Oak/Hornbeam is found on the London Clay, Beech on the Chalk and Ash/Maple on the Boulder Clay in the northeast of the county. There are, of course, local exceptions to these trends, particularly where small areas of woodland are involved.

Perhaps the most obvious sign of man's influence is shown in figure 3.5: the distribution of industrial, urban and suburban areas within the county. The major conurbations are clearly in the south of the county, along the Lea valley and in a broad band through the middle of the county from St. Albans through Hatfield, Welwyn Garden City and Stevenage to Letchworth and Hitchin. Substantial areas of the northeast of the county, between Ware and Royston are very sparsely populated.

Holes in the ground often form important bird habitats, particularly when they are wet, and in Hertfordshire most often result from gravel digging. Economically important gravel beds occur extensively in the Lea valley, Colne valley and the Vale of St. Albans and also in the Hitchin gap. Smaller deposits have also been worked in a number of valleys overlying the Chalk. Many of the pits in the Lea valley below Hoddesdon and in the Colne valley west of Rickmansworth are now largely exhausted and provide excellent complexes of wetland habitat. The main active gravel working areas are at present in the Vale of St. Albans and around Hertford where there are very extensive deposits. Figure 3.6 shows the distribution of extractive industry through the county. Although the major works are for gravel there are a few instances of chalk and clay pits. Dry pits are generally

16

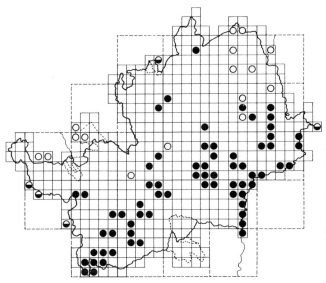

3.6 EXTRACTIVE INDUSTRIES

The marked tetrads include pits or quarries as detailed below:

- ● Sand and/or gravel
- ◕ Clay
- ○ Chalk

Both active and disused sand and gravel workings have been included but all the clay and chalk pits were probably active during the Atlas period. TQ09 L includes an active chalk pit as well as disused gravel workings.

filled in with refuse and returned to agricultural use immediately they are exhausted and some may have been filled in before the end of the survey. Figure 3.6 is therefore a summary of the recent gravel workings and does not necessarily represent the situation at any particular time.

Figure 3.7 shows the distribution of rivers, canals, streams and brooks in the county derived from the Ordnance Survey maps. The influence of geology is clearly apparent. On the Chalk and Clay-with-flints there are in general only well-defined rivers with no brooks or streams. In fact over much of the Chalk region there are many valleys which are completely dry. By way of contrast the Boulder Clay and London Clay regions have brooks and streams in every tetrad, even away from major river valleys. With an impervious substrate the poor drainage results in a complex network of small ditches and brooks. In the London Clay area another interesting phenomenon occurs. Due to the complex mixture of Pebble Gravel and clay deposits streams may appear in one area only to disappear a few kilometres away down a swallow hole. A well known example of this occurs at Water End, near North Mymms, where the Mymmshall Brook disappears into several holes.

Figure 3.8 shows the distribution of major lakes, as with most lowland counties, none are natural. Many small lakes on country estates were created during the eighteenth and nineteenth centuries when parklands were landscaped: good examples still exist at Brocket Park, Woodhall Park and the Broadwater Hatfield. The first large areas of open water were the feeder reservoirs needed to top-up the canals running through the county. The reservoirs at Aldenham and Tring are for this purpose and, even with the reduced level of traffic using the canals at present,

3.7 RIVERS AND STREAMS

The largest form of watercourse in each tetrad is shown by the dots as follows:

- ● River or canal
- ● Stream
- • Brook

In general rivers or canals are wider than five metres, streams are narrower and marked by a wide blue line on the 1:25000 maps; brooks are marked by the finest blue line.

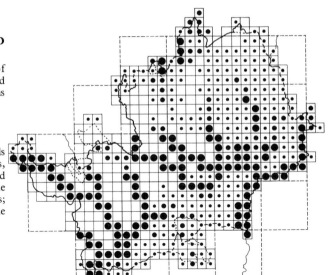

there may be water shortages in years of prolonged drought. The only large drinking water reservoir in the county is relatively modern: Hilfield Park which was filled about 25 years ago. The major sources of standing freshwater are wet gravel diggings which have been created over the last fifty years. These are concentrated in the lower Lea valley south of Hoddesdon and in the Colne valley west of Rickmansworth. Some have relatively uninteresting vertical banks but many have areas of lush marginal vegetation providing a haven for many different species of breeding birds. The range of habitats available in the county would be the poorer if all such pits were filled in and returned to agriculture.

3.8 OPEN WATER

The area of open water in any tetrad is shown by the dots as follows:

- ● More than 20 hectares
- ● Less than 20 hectares

Ponds shown on the 1:25000 maps as solid areas of dark blue, have been ignored for this assessment. All the areas shown are man-made and many are recent.

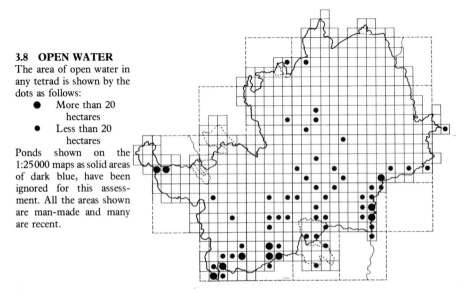

18

On the maps every small square is a tetrad. Each is given a letter (A to Z omitting O) which, with the 10-km square reference, uniquely determines which four km² area is being referred to. The map below (figure 4.1) shows how this works. The lettering system is that recommended by the Ray Society for work by naturalists, it is totally logical, for the successive letters refer to tetrads with increasing grid reference numbers (the south-western corner A is 00, B is 02 and Z is 88). On the outline map and throughout the atlas the current county boundary is shown by the thick solid line. Old boundaries are shown by pecked lines. The 504 tetrads surveyed are all enclosed on all four sides by continuous lines. All contain part of Hertfordshire and were surveyed in their entirety (not just 'our' part). Note that TQ09 D, TL01 D, TL11 E and TL12 A are outside the county and TQ09 A and TL30 Y were not surveyed.

All species maps have dots (or circles) in their tetrads according to the following codes:

- •   Possibly breeding
- ○   Probably or possibly breeding (generally records from the initial survey in 1967 but sometimes late records from observers notebooks)
- •   Probably breeding
- ●   Proved breeding

On all the published tetrad maps the records refer to the exact tetrad where the bird was recorded. None have been moved to protect sites but, in a few instances, no map has been published so as to protect a vulnerable species. In a few other cases the map has not been published since there are so few records that they may be easily described in the text.

4.1 MAP NOMEN-CLATURE
In the top left-hand corner of each 10-km square its two-letter, two-figure code is given. These are a standard feature of all modern Ordnance Survey maps. The lettering system for the 25 tetrads within each 10-km square is shown at the top left: note that letter O is omitted.

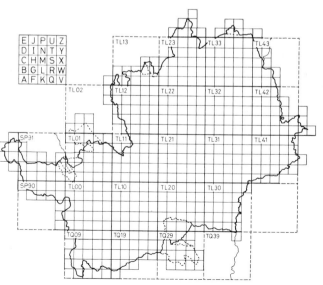

For every species for which breeding was proved during the Atlas period a range of standard information is given with each map (or illustration). To illustrate what these mean the example of Hawfinch is explained in detail below — the actual Hawfinch entries are on the left in italic:

Hertfordshire records from 109 tetrads 22%
During the Atlas period acceptable records of Hawfinch were received from 109 of the 504 tetrads — 22% of the total tetrads surveyed.

Bedfordshire 8%
The Bedfordshire Atlas (see page 125 for details), based also on tetrads, had records for Hawfinch from 8% of its tetrads.

London 9%
The London Atlas (see page 125), also using tetrads and including parts of south Hertfordshire, recorded Hawfinches from 9% of tetrads.

Kent 8%
Similarly the Kent Atlas recorded Hawfinch in 8% of tetrads.

Britain and Ireland 12%
The national Atlas, using 10-km squares as the basic recording unit, had Hawfinch records in 12% of squares. Obviously records are much more likely in bigger recording units and the 10-km striking rate for 33 squares containing any part of Hertfordshire is 67%.

France (Brittany) 39 (30)%
The French Atlas was based on map units measuring about 20 km x 27 km — more than five times the size of the British 10-km square. The national striking rate is given with, in brackets, the percentage for Brittany alone (also 20 km x 27 km units).

Netherlands 20%
The striking rate for the Dutch Atlas which used 5-km squares (a quarter the size of the British Atlas but still more than six times bigger than the tetrad). The fieldwork was carried out later than the other Atlases — from 1973-77. For all striking rates an entry of 0% means the species was present but in less than 0.5% of recording units. Entries marked — indicate there were no records.

Hertfordshire status: Breeding proved in 33 tetrads (30%) and suspected in 47 more (43%)

Local resident breeding bird, mainly in areas with some remnants of ancient woodlands.

The remaining entries refer only to Hertfordshire. First the proved breeding and probably breeding records are summarised and expressed as a percentage of all tetrads in which the species was recorded. These percentages vary from species to species and give an indication of how easy each is to record. Finally a brief statement of the bird's overall status in the county is given.

Many species are illustrated by Kevin Baker and most have a text about their Atlas information. This is often supplemented by small maps of habitat (wetlands, woods) or other features. Also inserted with the Atlas is a plastic sheet with a selection of such maps so that they may be used for comparative purposes. Extra ⊗ copies of this sheet are available for 25p (+ an S.A.E.) from C. J. M. at Tring. Larger scale copies of all the maps on the insert may be found in the earlier parts of the book.

Scattered through the book, particularly for the common passerines, are a series of population graphs derived from the local Common Bird Census plots. In most cases, a thick line shows the local plot information and a thinner one the national data. For most species the year 1966 is arbitrarily allotted a population index of 100 and a horizontal line is drawn through this level. The vertical scale is different for each species and depends on the range of population change but, in all cases, is a log scale. Sufficient values are plotted to allow easy interpretation. The horizontal scale is in years from 1962 to 1980. For the local plots all habitats were included, for the national information a particular habitat may have been selected: most are farmland, some woodland and, for a few species, both habitats are combined. We are most grateful to the census workers for their consistent efforts over the years and to the B.T.O. for making the raw data available.

The interpretation of the bird distribution maps, as indicated by our choice of habitat map to print beside them or the comments that we make, is often a matter of personal insight. We are sure that we have only started to scratch the surface in making comparisons of the sort we have here. You may well feel that we have got some of them wrong and quite probably you will find equally interesting similarities and differences as those we point out. Whatever happens these maps should make us better able to understand how Hertfordshire's breeding birds are distributed and identify those that are particularly vulnerable. Most birders would agree that one of the most important aspects of conservation is maintaining as many different species as possible in an area. The maps show an average of over 50 species present in each tetrad in the county: let us hope that the figure is as high or higher when we come to repeat the Atlas fieldwork in four or five years' time.

⊗ Stuck in between pages 12 and 13.

LITTLE GREBE   *Tachybaptus ruficollis*

Hertfordshire records from
87 tetrads	17%
Bedfordshire	14%
London	16%
Kent	10%
Britain & Ireland	49%
France (Brittany)	50(76)%
Netherlands	41%

Hertfordshire status:
Breeding proved in 64
tetrads (73%) and probable
in eight more (9%).

Widespread resident bird
of waters with emergent
vegetation. Some winter
concentrations.

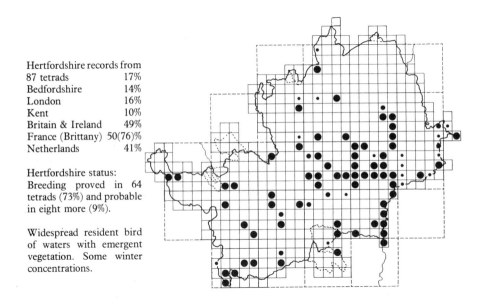

In Hertfordshire Little Grebes nest on many lakes and even large ponds where there are sheltered areas of marginal vegetation. Some pairs nest on canals and the wider reaches of the larger rivers and, perhaps surprisingly, breeding birds were even found in watercress beds. In many sites the birds are not easy to see and most of the Atlas records will originally have been logged by the recorder hearing the bird's characteristic whinnying call. There is little evidence of any recent change in the population resident in the county although, where gravel digging has created suitable habitat, there have undoubtedly been local increases. Most breeding sites retain their birds throughout the year although if the water freezes the birds must leave to find open conditions elsewhere. Many of the dots on tetrads with an isolated pond or lake will represent single pairs, but where there is a lot of water available dots may represent six or eight pairs.

GREAT CRESTED GREBE   *Podiceps cristatus*

Hertfordshire records from
27 tetrads   5%
Bedfordshire   11%
London   14%
Kent   5%
Britain & Ireland   26%
France (Brittany) 50(35)%
Netherlands   46%

Hertfordshire status:
Breeding proved in 24
tetrads (89%): no probable
breeding records.

Only found on larger
waters. Mobile outside
breeding season: large
flocks sometimes formed
may include immigrants.

The Great Crested Grebe needs fairly substantial water bodies on which to nest. As the map shows they are much more sparsely distributed than the Little Grebe with the major concentrations in the gravel pit areas and at the main reservoirs. This is one of the species that observers were asked to count. Since not all areas were counted in any one year the estimate, as with the other species, is an aggregate over the seven year period of the Atlas fieldwork. The sum of the maximum recorded from each tetrad, regardless of the year in which the records were made, was 69 pairs. This is the absolute maximum number of territories found. The species was horribly persecuted in the mid-nineteenth century for 'grebe-furs' and the 69 pairs is probably twice the total British population of 120 years ago. The first recorded nesting in Hertfordshire was at Tring Reservoirs in 1867 and the population there reached 75 pairs twenty years later: it may well have powered the spread of the species through England. Tring is still a local stronghold but there are several other waters which regularly hold half a dozen pairs.

Rivers and Streams   Lakes

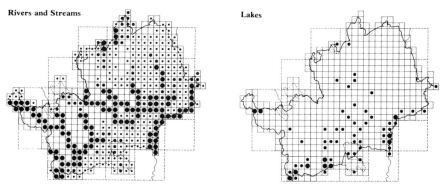

GREY HERON

Ardea cinerea

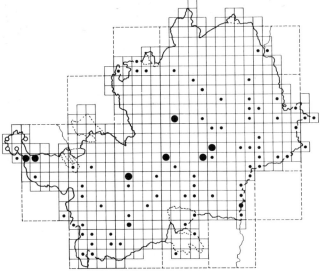

Hertfordshire records from
85 tetrads   17%
Bedfordshire   10%
London (proved)   1%
Kent   4%
Britain & Ireland   64%
France (Brittany) 23(13)%
Netherlands   34%

Hertfordshire status:
Breeding proved in seven
tetrads (8%) and probable
in two more (2%).

Resident colonial breeder
but immatures disperse. In
winter some Continental
immigrants may arrive.

Records of Herons during the breeding season were probably even more widespread than the map shows for many of the observers probably did not mark their cards for the odd Heron seen feeding. The main colonies during the Atlas period were at Wilstone (SP91 B) and Marsworth (SP91 G) with 11 or 12 pairs between them in several different years. In addition towards the end of the period the two colonies in TL21 held 14 pairs between them. Otherwise the breeding sites marked on the map held only one or two pairs. In recent years another Heronry has developed at Stockers Lake (TQ09 L). The Tring Reservoir colony is one of the very few in Britain where Herons breed in a reed-bed. In April and May of most years the young are visible on the nest from the causeway with its public footpath. There are major Heronries over the county boundary, at Walthamstow for example, from which many of the peripheral records of birds not proved to breed in the county may have originated. This is a species very badly affected by severe winters and as can be seen from the population graph (below) the Atlas data was gathered whilst the population was still recovering from the 1962-63 winters.

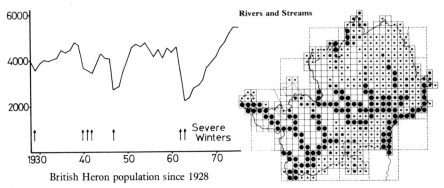

British Heron population since 1928

Rivers and Streams

MUTE SWAN

Cygnus olor

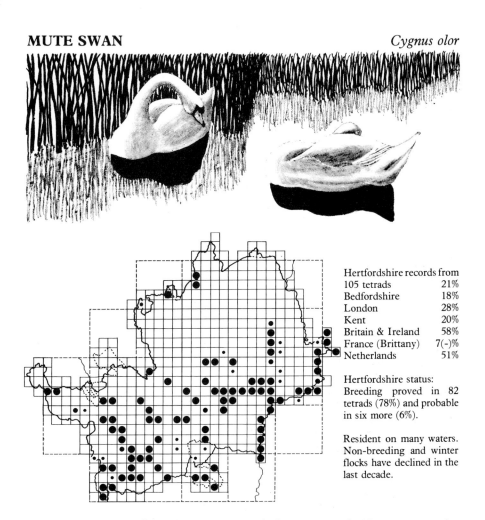

Hertfordshire records from
105 tetrads	21%
Bedfordshire	18%
London	28%
Kent	20%
Britain & Ireland	58%
France (Brittany)	7(-)%
Netherlands	51%

Hertfordshire status:
Breeding proved in 82 tetrads (78%) and probable in six more (6%).

Resident on many waters. Non-breeding and winter flocks have declined in the last decade.

Mute Swans in Hertfordshire nest as regularly on waters in city centres as on islands in inaccessible gravel pits. In many situations they are fed by man and, regrettably, may suffer at the hands of vandals. Most of the large water bodies have breeding pairs and many reaches of the wider rivers and stretches of canal are also occupied. Breeding is very easily proved although the unfledged young may be moved several kilometres by their parents. The aggregate number of pairs (different territories occupied) over the years 1967-73 was roughly 120. This may represent a slight decrease over the previous ten years when the British Mute Swan population was at its peak. Since the Atlas period the decline has continued and is related to the ingestion by the birds of lead (both split-shot and weights) lost or discarded by fishermen. Birds which occupy waters with a good growth of bottom weed do not seem to be at risk but those on waters with unvegetated bottoms and where there is a lot of coarse fishing often display the classic symptoms of lead poisoning: the neck held back with a lump at its base. These birds will generally lose their co-ordination, become lethargic and ultimately die.

25

CANADA GOOSE

Branta canadensis

Hertfordshire records from

14 tetrads	3%
Bedfordshire	9%
London	9%
Kent	7%
Britain & Ireland	18%
France (Brittany)	-%
Netherlands	1%

Hertfordshire status:
Breeding proved in five tetrads (36%) and probable in three more (21%).

Feral birds, some tame, now breed on several large waters. Mobile in winter when the flocks may feed well away from breeding sites.

Canada Geese have been established as breeding species over large areas of the North, Midlands, East Anglia and Southeast England for many years. It is therefore rather surprising that no breeding attempts were recorded in Hertfordshire until 1965 — unsuccessful in the Colne valley. Well established groups of birds are now breeding in rather more areas than shown on the map. Some may result from local releases — certainly the Tring birds were very tame when they first appeared — but many must result from the natural spread of this successful introduction.

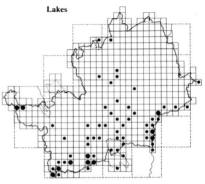

Lakes

GREYLAG GOOSE

Anser anser

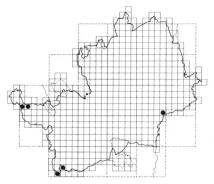

Hertfordshire records from six tetrads			1%
Bedfordshire	5%	Britain & Ireland	5%
London	1%	France (Brittany)	0(-)%
Kent	1%	Netherlands	4%

Hertfordshire status:
Breeding proved in five tetrads (83%): no probable breeding records.

The county's population of breeding Greylags mostly result from birds released in the last twenty years. In some areas they flock with the Canadas but elsewhere they are to be found on their breeding waters throughout the year. They are steadily increasing and pioneering new sites.

MANDARIN

Aix galericulata

Hertfordshire records from three tetrads			1%
Bedfordshire	1%	Britain & Ireland	1%
London	4%	France (Brittany)	-%
Kent	0%	Netherlands	0%

Hertfordshire status:
Breeding proved in one tetrad (33%) and probable in one more (33%).

A popular species in wildfowl collections small colonies have been established in various parts of Britain. The Hertfordshire records may result from such escapes or the expansion of birds from the main English breeding area in Surrey where, centred on the River Mole, 200 - 300 pairs breed.

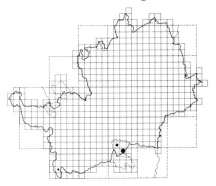

This species generally nests in holes high in large trees. It is therefore most likely to be found breeding at ponds or lakes surrounded by trees. Drakes prospecting for nest sites in the early spring have been shot by astonished pigeon shooters in mistake for their legitimate quarry. Gradual colonisation of suitable areas in the future is possible: prospecting birds (a pair) were present one recent spring on the Ashridge Estate near Tring.

GADWALL

Anas strepera

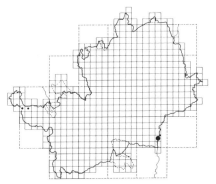

Hertfordshire records from three tetrads			1%
Bedfordshire	-%	Britain & Ireland	4%
London	1%	France (Brittany)	3(6)%
Kent	1%	Netherlands	17%

Hertfordshire status:
Breeding proved in one tetrad (33%): no probable breeding records.

Two breeding records — Tring 1928 and Cheshunt 1969. This duck is a regular passage and winter visitor to several of the larger waters in the county and spring and summer records are not unusual. The major British concentration of breeding birds is in the Brecklands of Suffolk and Norfolk.

TEAL

Anas crecca

Hertfordshire records from 11 tetrads			2%
Bedfordshire	5%	Britain & Ireland	46%
London	2%	France (Brittany)	16(24)%
Kent	4%	Netherlands	54%

Hertfordshire status:
Breeding proved in one tetrad (9%) and probable in one more (9%).

Breeding used to be regular but is now not often recorded although birds are frequently seen during the summer. Outside the breeding season Teal may be found on almost any suitable marshy site. Large numbers come to Britain for the winter from all over Northern Europe.

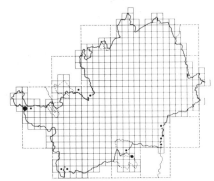

SHOVELER

Anas clypeata

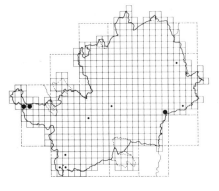

Hertfordshire records from ten tetrads			2%
Bedfordshire	4%	Britain & Ireland	15%
London	2%	France (Brittany)	10(18)%
Kent	5%	Netherlands	62%

Hertfordshire status:
Breeding proved in three tetrads (30%): no probable breeding records.

For many years the Shoveler has been a regular breeding species at Tring Reservoirs and they now also breed in the Lea valley. Winter and passage birds may be found, sometimes in good numbers, on most of the pits, lakes and reservoirs with shallow and sheltered margins.

Wintering birds often remain well into April and, since pairs may be formed during the winter, their display may sometimes raise false hopes of breeding. The annual records of 20, 30 or even 40 pairs displaying at Tring must almost always be of migrants since the breeding population is currently only one or two pairs.

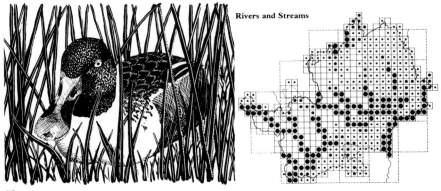

Rivers and Streams

MALLARD

Anas platyrhynchos

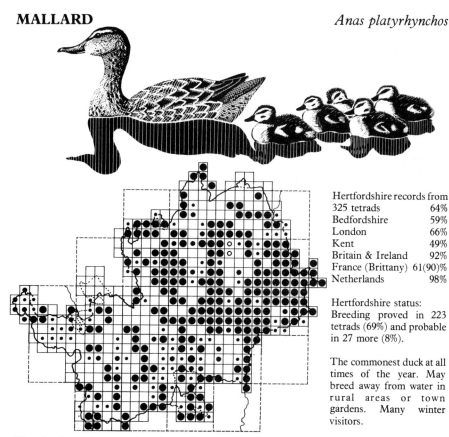

Hertfordshire records from

325 tetrads	64%
Bedfordshire	59%
London	66%
Kent	49%
Britain & Ireland	92%
France (Brittany)	61(90)%
Netherlands	98%

Hertfordshire status:
Breeding proved in 223 tetrads (69%) and probable in 27 more (8%).

The commonest duck at all times of the year. May breed away from water in rural areas or town gardens. Many winter visitors.

The Mallard is second only to the Moorhen as Hertfordshire's most common breeding water bird. Nesting birds may be found in all but the very driest areas. The C.B.C. indices, shown opposite, indicate that the county's population has been increasing over the last 15 years in step with the rest of Britain. In the mid-1960's this may have been the recovery from losses caused by the cold winters but numbers may now be supplemented by birds reared and released by wildfowlers.

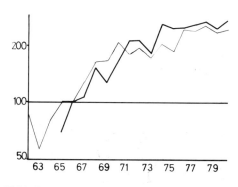

Thick line: local C.B.C., thin: national (farmland).

GARGANEY

Anas querquedula

Three Atlas records all 'column 1': one at Tring (SP91 G) and two in the Lea valley (TL30 R & T). In the past has bred twice: Tring 1928 and Aldenham 1931. Recorded annually on passage.

POCHARD

Aythya ferina

Hertfordshire records from
24 tetrads	5%
Bedfordshire	7%
London	6%
Kent	5%
Britain & Ireland	15%
France (Brittany)	11(24)%
Netherlands	27%

Hertfordshire status:
Breeding proved in eight tetrads (33%) and probable in six more (25%).

Generally only breeds on larger waters but may be found on others at all times of the year: many winter visitors.

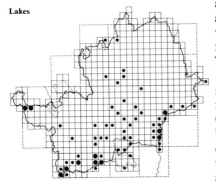

Lakes

A rather scarce breeding bird always associated with the more major waters although the nests may be in dense vegetation beside small ponds a few yards from the main lake. The breeding birds at Tring have been established since about 1850 but the other sites are much more recent. Breeding in the Lea valley became regular about twenty years ago and the Colne valley population is in the process of becoming fully established. Birds are quite regularly seen during the summer at waters where they do not breed. Pochard are undoubtedly slowly increasing as a nesting species in Hertfordshire and in England in general.

TUFTED DUCK

Aythya fuligula

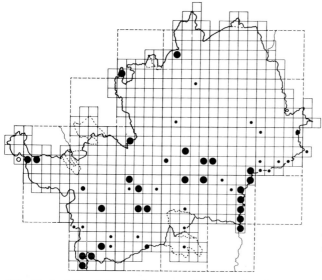

Hertfordshire records from
53 tetrads 11%
Bedfordshire 17%
London 22%
Kent 6%
Britain & Ireland 42%
France (Brittany) 4(9)%
Netherlands 52%

Hertfordshire status:
Breeding proved in 26
tetrads (49%) and probable
in four more (8%).

Breeds on most lakes and
reservoirs and even some
rivers. Large influx in
winter with birds on all
deeper waters.

The Tufted Duck is much more widespread and numerous as a breeding species
than the Pochard and may sometimes be found nesting on small lakes or rivers.
Some waters hold small colonies of nesting birds but in Hertfordshire these are
never more than about 15 pairs. Elsewhere in Britain, on large lakes with islands
for nesting, hundreds of pairs may breed. The Tufted Duck is a recent colonist of
Britain with the first breeding record in 1849 in Yorkshire. The first Hertfordshire
nest was at Tring in 1893. The population is still expanding and with the increased
availability of waters through gravel digging, looks set to continue to do so for
many years yet. During the breeding season, as with many other ducks, the drakes
may form small flocks whilst the females are incubating their eggs. The nests are
generally in tangled vegetation a few yards from the water's edge and several may
be close together — particularly if the birds are able to breed on an island
protected from foxes.

RUDDY DUCK

Oxyura jamaicensis

Hertfordshire records from one tetrad		0%
Bedfordshire	-% Britain & Ireland	1%
London	-% France (Brittany)	-%
Kent	-% Netherlands	0%

Hertfordshire status:
Breeding proved in one tetrad (100%).

The feral British population of this American
species is based in the West Midlands. It was
established about 25 years ago by birds which had
escaped from wildfowl collections. The birds
regularly breeding at Tring since 1965 were, at the
time of the Atlas, the southeastern outpost of the
species.

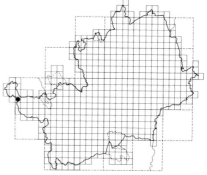

SPARROWHAWK

Accipiter nisus

Hertfordshire records from
43 tetrads   9%
Bedfordshire   6%
London   6%
Kent   2%
Britain & Ireland   68%
France (Brittany)   62(68)%
Netherlands   34%

Hertfordshire status:
Breeding proved in three
tetrads (7%) and probable
in ten more (23%).

A scarce resident species at
the time of the Atlas: a
result of pesticide use on
farmland. Now widespread
and becoming quite
common.

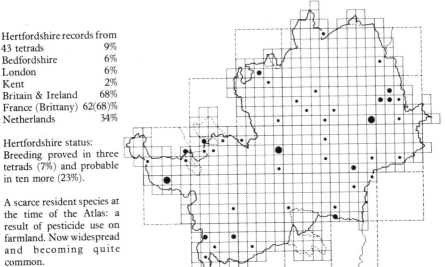

The breeding Sparrowhawks in Britain seem to be sedentary but may hunt over quite a wide area. Adjacent dots on the map may thus represent a single bird or pair. This was almost certainly a numerous bird over large parts of the county many years ago but, first through the attention of game-keepers and then through the effects of pesticides, has been reduced to become very scarce indeed. The map probably shows the Sparrowhawk just after its lowest ebb. Certainly there are indications all over the county that it has increased greatly over the last ten years. This has followed statutory and voluntary controls on the use of the most toxic organo-chlorine pesticides. Detailed studies in the Tring area now regularly reveal two dozen active nests over an area of about 100 km².

BUZZARD

Buteo buteo

Hertfordshire records from six tetrads		1%
Bedfordshire 1%	Britain & Ireland	38%
London -%	France (Brittany)	80(72)%
Kent -%	Netherlands	45%

Hertfordshire status:
Preeding proved in one tetrad (17%): no probable
breeding records.

Probably a resident breeding bird until 100 years ago the Buzzard is now regularly recorded throughout the year. The Atlas breeding record (possibly the same pair for two years) was in the western half of the county. Unfortunately almost all records are still of single birds.

HOBBY

Falco subbuteo

Hertfordshire records from 23 tetrads			5%
Bedfordshire	9%	Britain & Ireland	7%
London	2%	France (Brittany)	37(34)%
Kent	1%	Netherlands	51%

Hertfordshire status:
Breeding proved in ten tetrads (43%) and probable in two more (9%).

Considered not to have bred since 1884; regular breeding has been recorded since 1967. All the pairs proved to breed were in the main wooded areas of the county. Young birds are frequently reported preying on hirundines at autumn roosts.

KESTREL

Falco tinnunculus

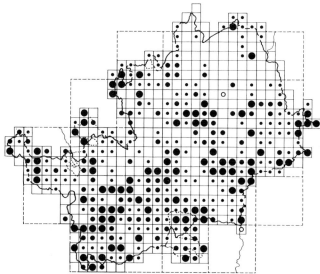

Hertfordshire records from

335 tetrads	66%
Bedfordshire	65%
London	79%
Kent	42%
Britain & Ireland	92%
France (Brittany)	93(99)%
Netherlands	92%

Hertfordshire status:
Breeding proved in 90 tetrads (27%) and probable in 87 more (26%).

The commonest raptor at all times of the year. Breeds in all areas (including the towns). Mobile outside the breeding season with many immigrants.

Breeding Kestrels may regularly be found nesting in towns, suburban areas and in the country. Ledges on buildings may be used but in Hertfordshire the natural site is a shallow hole or crevice in a tree — often where a branch has broken. The map shows few Kestrels in the northern part of the county where the agricultural land is predominantly arable. These open areas lack both nest sites and also hedges used as winter refuges by the bird's prey — small mammals. Nationally the C.B.C. index shows a steady population level from 1968 following a recovery after the bad winters of 1962-63. The local index, based on very small samples, seems to show that the population over the last few years is rather higher than during the Atlas period.

33

RED-LEGGED PARTRIDGE *Alectoris rufa*

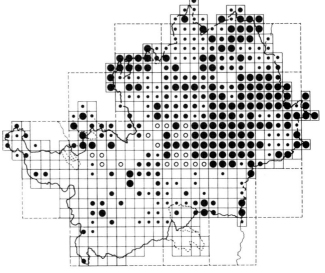

Hertfordshire records from
337 tetrads	67%
Bedfordshire	77%
London	22%
Kent	16%
Britain & Ireland	24%
France (Brittany)	44(26)%
Netherlands	1%

Hertfordshire status:
Breeding proved in 141 tetrads (42%) and probable in 82 more (24%).

Widespread as a resident having first been introduced to Britain 300 years ago: some are reared.

This species, still called the French Partridge in some areas, has been introduced into Britain many times over the last 300 years. The first successes which may have affected Hertfordshire were probably at the end of the eighteenth century. By the end of the nineteenth century they were locally common in the northern part of the county but , as recently as 1959 (when Bryan Sage published his book), it was considerably less numerous than the native Grey Partridge. During the last 20 years, as the C.B.C. indices show, Red-legs have fared much better than Grey and over much of the north of the county the Red-leg is now by far the commoner of the two. This is one of the few species nesting in Britain that lays two clutches: one is incubated by the male and the other by the female.

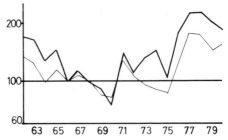

Thick line: local C.B.C., thin: national (farmland).

34

GREY PARTRIDGE   *Perdix perdix*

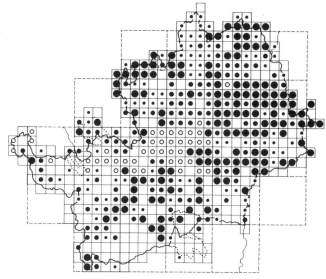

Hertfordshire records from
376 tetrads   75%
Bedfordshire   61%
London   41%
Kent   55%
Britain & Ireland   59%
France (Brittany) 51(78)%
Netherlands   92%

Hertfordshire status:
Breeding proved in 143
tetrads (38%) and probable
in 105 more (28%).

Widespread, but declining,
resident. A native species
less easily reared for release
than the introduced Red-
leg.

Rather more widespread than the Red-legged Partridge and resident in areas with smaller fields this species suffered a marked decline in the early 1960's. This has been related to the use of insecticides in cereal crops which reduced (or eliminated) the food needed by the hatchlings. The local C.B.C. index has fallen more steeply than the national one. This may be related to the more intensive cultivation of cereals in Hertfordshire than in the majority of Britain.

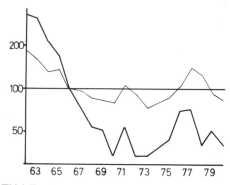

Thick line: local C.B.C., thin: national (farmland).

QUAL

Coturnix coturnix

Hertfordshire records from
34 tetrads   7%
Bedfordshire   6%
London   1%
Kent   3%
Britain & Ireland 11%
France (Brittany) 66(49)%
Netherlands   25%

Hertfordshire status:
Breeding proved in four
tetrads (12%) and probable
in 20 more (59%).

Scarce summer visitor:
regular in a few favoured
areas but marked influxes
occur every few years.

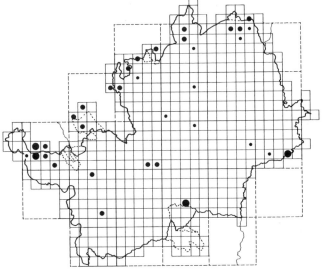

This attractive little gamebird is the only member of its group to migrate a long distance to (or from) Britain. It winters in Africa and often does not reach us until June. In Hertfordshire it was formerly fairly common but seems to have decreased during the last century with very few records from about 1890 to 1935. Since then it has been recorded regularly in very small numbers and irregularly, in particular years, in fairly large numbers. The first of the special years was 1938 and we were lucky to have a notable one, 1970, during the Atlas period. Many of the records are 'column 2' for it is very easy to record the territorial males with their 'Wet-my-lips' song but very difficult to prove breeding. Most records were in or near the traditional areas for the species along the Chiltern scarp but isolated birds were found in other areas both in cereals and on grass — even water meadows. A few Quail are sometimes released on shoots but this is not thought to have affected this Atlas map.

36

PHEASANT

Phasianus colchicus

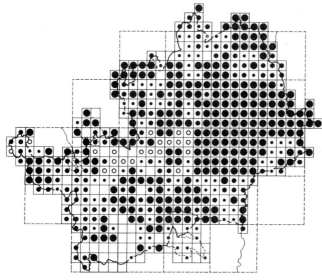

Hertfordshire records from
459 tetrads   91%
Bedfordshire   84%
London   51%
Kent   59%
Britain & Ireland 80%
France (Brittany) 71(64)%
Netherlands   96%

Hertfordshire status:
Breeding proved in 250
tetrads (54%) and probable
in 104 more (23%).

Abundant long-established
introduced gamebird still
reared and released in very
large numbers.

In many areas the Pheasant is (or was formerly) by far the most important species economically. There are still many parts of the county where much of the land management is influenced by its needs. Apart from the damage that this may do to the natural predators (both feathered and furred) this game management is almost always beneficial to other bird populations. Even where reared birds are released their feeding places often swarm with small seed-eating species.

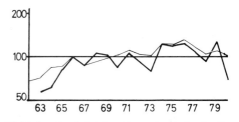

Thick line: local C.B.C., thin: national (farmland).

LADY AMHERST'S PHEASANT

Chrysolophus amherstiae

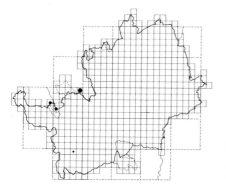

Hertfordshire records from four tetrads   1%
Bedfordshire 9%   Britain & Ireland   0%
London   0%   France (Brittany)   -%
Kent   -%   Netherlands   -%

Hertfordshire status:
Breeding proved in one tetrad (25%) and probable
in two more (50%).

Established at the turn of the century from releases
in Bedfordshire this spectacular, but very shy, bird
generally keeps to deep cover. They are thus
difficult to record except by call in spring. The
birds on the Bedfordshire border are the southern
outpost of the main British population still centred
on Woburn.

WATER RAIL   *Rallus aquaticus*

Hertfordshire records from
30 tetrads   6%
Bedfordshire   3%
London   4%
Kent   4%
Britain & Ireland   24%
France (Brittany) 45(81)%
Netherlands   39%

Hertfordshire status:
Breeding proved in five
tetrads (17%) and probable
in 14 more (47%).

Uncommon breeding
species of rank, wet cover.
Many winter visitors swell
the population.

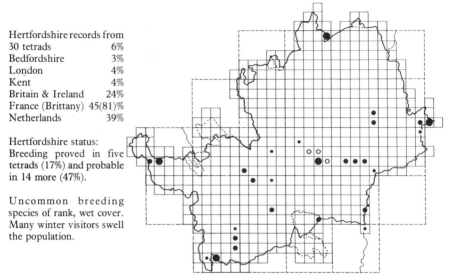

This elusive species often only makes its presence known during the breeding season by its unearthly screaming calls. This sound, known as 'sharming' and often likened to the death cries of a stuck pig, can sometimes be heard in the late winter and early spring when it may be uttered by winter visitors soon to leave for their European nesting area. However there are certainly summering birds which regularly breed at several sites through the county. All the breeding areas are wet and most have extensive waterbodies near them but the Water Rail seldom emerges from the dense marginal vegetation where it nests. Until about 20 years ago there had been few summer records and only a handful of sites had been suspected of holding breeding birds. During the Atlas fieldwork many sites were found where breeding had never before been suspected and it seems probable that the species has slowly increased as a nesting bird over the last 20-30 years.

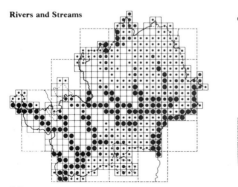

Rivers and Streams

38

SPOTTED CRAKE

Porzana porzana

Hertfordshire records from one tetrad		0%
Bedfordshire -%	Britain & Ireland	1%
London -%	France (Brittany)	8(8)%
Kent -%	Netherlands	8%

Hertfordshire status:
Breeding proved in one tetrad (100%).

The only Hertfordshire breeding record was in 1967 when young were reared near Wheathampstead. Otherwise a rare visitor mostly recorded in the autumn: some remaining for several weeks within the same small patch of damp vegetation.

CORNCRAKE

Crex crex

Hertfordshire records from six tetrads	1%
Bedfordshire	0%
London	-%
Kent	3%
Britain & Ireland	39%
France (Brittany)	17(19)%
Netherlands	10%

Hertfordshire status:
Breeding probable in three tetrads (50%).

Formerly widespread as a summer visitor to hayfields. Now very scarce on passage.

The sad decline of this intriguing species over the whole of western Europe has happened over the last hundred years. From being a fairly common summer visitor over most of the area, including Hertfordshire, it has now become a very rare bird everywhere except along the western edge — in the Western Isles of Scotland and in Ireland. The reason for its demise is easily understood for with changes in agricultural practice and the improved strains of grass, hay cutting now occurs much earlier in the spring. The Corncrakes, most of which breed in hayfields, do not have time to complete their nesting cycle before the fields are mown. The nest (or tiny young) are then either destroyed by the machinery or left exposed to predation. Unfortunately there was no evidence that any of the birds mapped were able to breed successfully, although at least one of the 'column 2' records was of a bird persistently craking over a period of six weeks. Some of the residents of a nearby row of cottages welcomed the mowing of the field and the subsequent peaceful nights!

39

MOORHEN

Gallinula chloropus

Hertfordshire records from
399 tetrads %	79%
Bedfordshire	70%
London	68%
Kent	63%
Britain & Ireland	82%
France (Brittany)	
	78(100)%
Netherlands	94%

Hertfordshire status:
Breeding proved in 320
tetrads (80%) and probable
in 18 more (5%).

Widespread resident bird
on any water-body: stream,
ditch, pond, lake or river.
Some winter visitors.

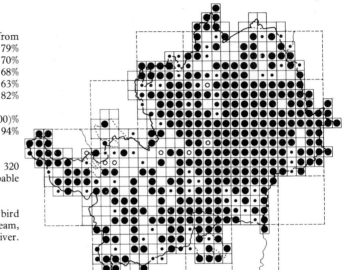

Moorhens may be found wherever there is water. Most sites in the chalky and well-drained northeast of the county are where Moorhens nest happily on farm ponds or similar restricted waters. In a few very dry years they are frustrated as the ponds may dry out completely, but with the first rains and the refilling of the sites the Moorhens will return. Over most of southern Britain this is a fairly confiding species and easily recorded but in northern Britain there are still some pairs which behave in the very circumspect manner of the smaller crakes: even these were readily recorded for the National Atlas as the characteristic 'pwark' call gives their presence away. The national C.B.C. index shows a marked decline over the cold winters in 1962-63. This will be an effect of the cold itself and may also show that foxes were able to cross ice to get weakened birds in normally secure roosting sites. Both the local and national indices indicate a fairly steady and healthy population over the last 10-15 years.

Lakes

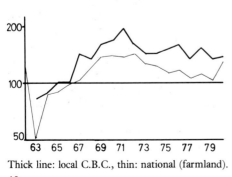

Thick line: local C.B.C., thin: national (farmland).

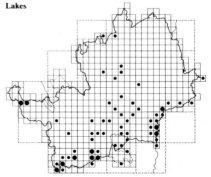

COOT   *Fulica atra*

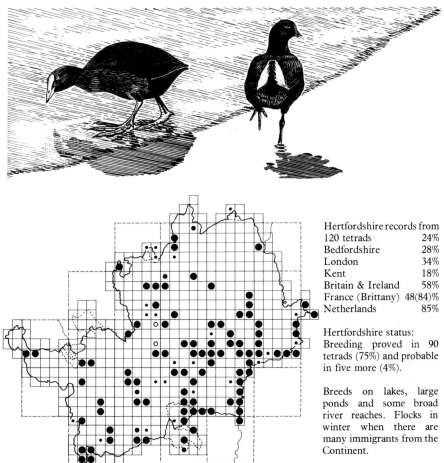

Hertfordshire records from
120 tetrads   24%
Bedfordshire   28%
London   34%
Kent   18%
Britain & Ireland   58%
France (Brittany) 48(84)%
Netherlands   85%

Hertfordshire status:
Breeding proved in 90
tetrads (75%) and probable
in five more (4%).

Breeds on lakes, large
ponds and some broad
river reaches. Flocks in
winter when there are
many immigrants from the
Continent.

Coot are generally confined to the larger waters, over 0.5 hectares in extent, where there are open areas allowing them to dive and collect their vegetable food from the bottom. Where conditions are ideal many pairs may breed on the same lake and outside the breeding season large flocks may form. The Coot has increased in Hertfordshire as more gravel pits have been dug and reservoirs built. Some smaller lakes, where breeding has taken place in the past, may gradually become unsuitable as the bottom silts up and emergent vegetation spreads to cover the water area. In such circumstances Moorhens, Little Grebes and Mallard may thrive but Coot and most ducks, certainly the diving species, will not remain. Historical records show that the Tring Reservoirs were the main area for this species, as for so many other water birds, during the nineteenth century. Sage records that the Hon. Walter Rothschild considered that 200 pairs bred in 1887 — currently the annual total is nearer 20.

41

LITTLE RINGED PLOVER *Charadrius dubius*

Hertfordshire records from
27 tetrads	5%
Bedfordshire	6%
London	8%
Kent	2%
Britain & Ireland	7%
France (Brittany)	25(42)%
Netherlands	25%

Hertfordshire status:
Breeding proved in 23 tetrads (85%) and probable in two more (7%).

A recent colonist from the Continent, this summer visitor generally breeds in gravel pits.

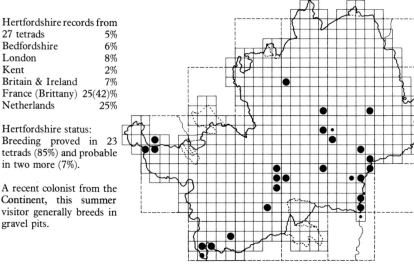

The National Atlas shows that this attractive little wader now breeds in Britain east of the line from the Dee to the Solent and south of the line from Morecambe Bay to the Farne Islands (with one breeding record in the Scottish Lowlands). The very first British breeding records were in Hertfordshire with one pair at Tring in 1938 and two there in 1944 (when there was another pair in Middlesex). On the Continent this is a species nesting mainly in the gravel fans exposed in summer along the beds of major rivers — not a habitat much found in southern England. However the open exposed substrate of gravel pits, even those actively being quarried, has proved to be an acceptable substitute and this is generally where they are found breeding. In Hertfordshire exposed areas in sewage works have also been used and just north of Tring birds have fairly regularly been found nesting on the floors of chalk-pits: once actually between the tracks of the works railway! The graph below shows the national increase in numbers: over the Atlas period an aggregate total of about 25 territories were occupied.

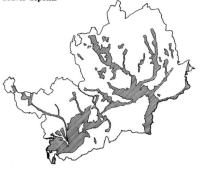

Gravel deposits

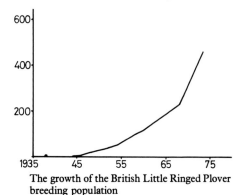

The growth of the British Little Ringed Plover breeding population

RINGED PLOVER

Charadrius hiaticula

Hertfordshire records from two tetrads			0%
Bedfordshire	3%	Britain & Ireland	32%
London	1%	France (Brittany)	1(9)%
Kent	6%	Netherlands	16%

Hertfordshire status:
Breeding probable in two tetrads (100%).

Generally a coastal breeding species in England it has nested twice in Hertfordshire: Rye Meads 1957 and Amwell 1976. With its colonisation of gravel pits in East Anglia it should soon become established in the county. Regularly recorded, at suitable sites, on passage.

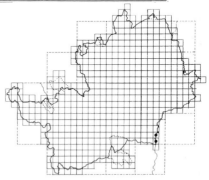

STONE CURLEW

Burhinus oedicnemus

Hertfordshire records from 12 tetrads			2%
Bedfordshire	1%	Britain & Ireland	2%
London	-%	France (Brittany)	23(2)%
Kent	0%	Netherlands	0%

Hertfordshire status:
Breeding proved in six tetrads (50%) and probable in four more (33%).

Formerly bred along the length of the Chiltern Scarp but now confined, as a regular breeding bird, to the open country near Royston. The Hertfordshire population nests successfully on farmland. A summer visitor from March to October.

The Stone Curlew is really a bird of the arid desert and semi-desert parts of the southern Palearctic. In Britain it has always been restricted to dry, open areas but has declined nationally over the last 100 years. The remaining area in Hertfordshire with a good population is near Royston and contributed seven of the Atlas records. Three more (all column 2) came from the Pirton area from whence there have only been a handful of casual records over the last decade. The other two records were of birds proved breeding on the fringe of the Royston area and a territorial bird in TL32 in one year only.

LAPWING

Vanellus vanellus

Hertfordshire records from
355 tetrads   70%
Bedfordshire   69%
London   35%
Kent   48%
Britain & Ireland   85%
France (Brittany) 40(58)%
Netherlands   97%

Hertfordshire status:
Breeding proved in 154
tetrads (43%) and probable
in 75 more (21%).

A widespread but patchily
distributed breeding
species of open farmland.
Flocks from June to March
may include immigrants.

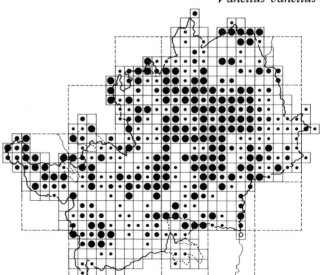

Lapwings may breed in many different habitats but always in open areas. In Hertfordshire these will typically be fairly large farm fields and generally on arable. However a comparison between the species map and the distribution of arable (see below) shows that this link does not explain everything. In the damper parts of the county there are a few areas with quite dense nesting populations on water meadows. The open ground provided by gravel and chalk pits is often used and a few pairs may nest in permanent pasture even in dry areas. The C.B.C. index figures show, nationally, that there was a gradual recovery during the 1960's from the effects of the two severe winters. Locally the C.B.C. shows a worrying decline over the 1970's. Research by the Populations Section of the B.T.O. indicates that this decline is typical of southern and eastern England whilst populations in the north and west seem to be thriving. Once more this seems to be a result of the increasingly intensive cultivation of cereals in the southeast.

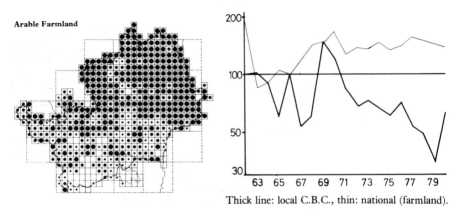

Arable Farmland

Thick line: local C.B.C., thin: national (farmland).

SNIPE

Gallinago gallinago

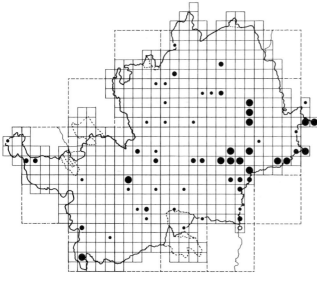

Hertfordshire records from
58 tetrads	12%
Bedfordshire	16%
London	6%
Kent	8%
Britain & Ireland	81%
France (Brittany)	18(40)%
Netherlands	61%

Hertfordshire status:
Breeding proved in 16 tetrads (28%) and probable in 17 more (29%).

An uncommon breeding bird of damp meadows in Hertfordshire. Much more widespread and numerous in the winter.

The Snipe is a bird which many Hertfordshire birdwatchers expect to see in the winter but not in the summer. In fact it was probably a fairly widespread breeding bird over the whole county (apart from the chalk) until the obsessive drainage of damp areas for agricultural purposes over the last 30 or 40 years reduced the suitable nesting areas so drastically. A few new sites have been provided by man's activities including the damp bottoms of some gravel pits and the partly flooded fringes of one or two of the reservoirs — note the two tetrads in SP91 which record drumming birds at Tring reservoirs. Most of the other tetrads are river valley sites where water meadows still form the major habitat. Unfortunately, even during the Atlas period, some of these were lost through further drainage and the situation now is considerably worse. This sorry state of affairs is general to much of England and Wales and is attracting a considerable amount of attention at the moment. Efforts are being made to protect the remaining sites through purchase or management agreements by both the County Naturalists' Trusts and the R.S.P.B.

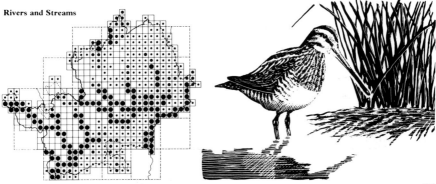

Rivers and Streams

WOODCOCK   *Scolopax rusticola*

Hertfordshire records from
106 tetrads	21%
Bedfordshire	21%
London	9%
Kent	8%
Britain & Ireland	57%
France (Brittany)	20(7)%
Netherlands	28%

Hertfordshire status:
Breeding proved in 12
tetrads (11%) and probable
in 68 more (64%).

Commonly holding terri-
tory in areas of major
woodlands: numbers
augmented by winter
visitors from the
Continent.

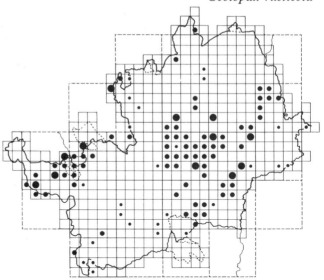

Most of the major woodland areas in the county have breeding Woodcock in them.
The spectacular crepuscular display flights of the males, called roding, were
responsible for the majority of the 'Probably breeding' records. Recent research
has shown that these birds are patrolling an area looking for a female with whom to
mate. When they find one they stay with her whilst she lays her clutch and then,
leaving her to incubate it, they will start roding again in the hope of finding a
second female. Although breeding has often been recorded in conifers the more
open and mixed under-storey in deciduous woodland provides a better nesting
and feeding habitat. The provisional results of a Hertfordshire Natural History
Society survey of the species in summer 1981 indicate that there has been a very
serious decrease in the numbers breeding in the county over the last ten years.
Some areas with many Atlas records failed to provide more than a handful of
roding birds. Whilst it is possible that 1981 was simply a single bad year the future
outlook for the Woodcock as a Hertfordshire breeding species does not look too
good.

Semi-natural Woodland

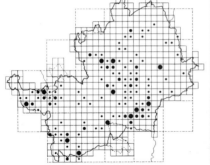

CURLEW

Numenius arquata

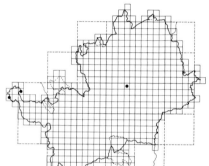

Hertfordshire records from three tetrads		1%
Bedfordshire -%	Britain & Ireland	72%
London -%	France (Brittany)	13(16)%
Kent -%	Netherlands	48%

Hertfordshire status:
Breeding probable in three tetrads (100%).

Not yet proved to breed in Hertfordshire although the eastward spread through Buckinghamshire has been responsible for the records of territorial birds in Hertfordshire tetrads on the Gault. Regularly recorded on passage.

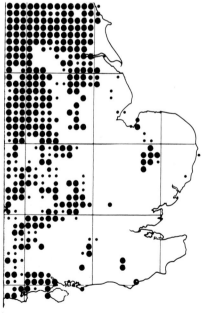

The National Atlas (10 km squares) for Curlew in eastern England

When Bryan Sage published his book in 1959 there was no hint that the Curlew might reach Hertfordshire as a breeding bird. He noted it as 'a common spring and autumn passage migrant, not often alighting'. It certainly remains this but also now breeds regularly in the Buckinghamshire part of the Vale of Aylesbury. Territorial birds in tetrads including Hertfordshire were responsible for the two western dots on the map and it seems very likely that breeding has taken place in the tetrads, if not in the county. In TL21 U a pair of Curlew were regularly recorded in one year. The map shown on the right is from the National Atlas and shows the Curlew's distribution in the eastern part of England. The heath breeding birds in Hampshire, Sussex and the East Anglian Brecks were first recorded 40 or 50 years ago and the farmland breeding population through Gloucester, Wiltshire, Oxford and Buckingham has spread eastwards for 60 to 70 years.

47

REDSHANK

Tringa totanus

Hertfordshire records from

23 tetrads	5%
Bedfordshire	8%
London	6%
Kent	16%
Britain & Ireland	50%
France (Brittany)	4(6)%
Netherlands	72%

Hertfordshire status:
Breeding proved in ten
tetrads (43%) and probable
in seven more (30%).

An uncommon breeding
bird of water meadows and
gravel pits now almost
confined to the Lea
catchment. Regular at
many sites on passage and
during the winter.

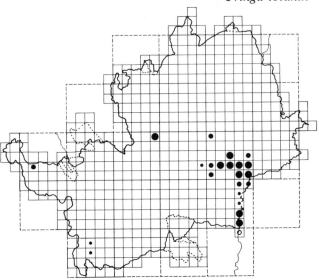

River Systems

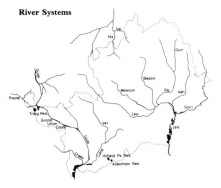

Formerly Redshank could be found
breeding in suitable sites all over the
county. Over the last 30 years or so those
sites have dwindled through drainage and
the Redshank itself seems to have become
even scarcer. The cold winters of 1962 and
1963 certainly caused the species heavy
mortality from which, at least locally, it
has never fully recovered. At the time of
the Atlas virtually all breeding records
were from the Lea and its water meadows
and gravel pits. In the last few years the
decline had undoubtedly continued and
very few pairs still nest with us.

COMMON SANDPIPER

Actitis hypoleucos

Hertfordshire records from seven tetrads			1%
Bedfordshire	0%	Britain & Ireland	48%
London	2%	France (Brittany)	20(-)%
Kent	-%	Netherlands	8%

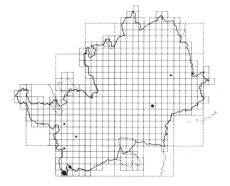

Hertfordshire status:
Breeding proved in one tetrad (14%) and probable in two more (29%).

Very irregular as a breeding species: only two in the last 20 years which were at Hertford 1961 and Rickmansworth 1967. However regularly recorded on passage from March to October with birds present in some areas throughout the summer.

COMMON TERN

Sterna hirundo

The Common Tern is a recent colonist having first been recorded breeding in 1966 at Broxbourne. This followed suspected breeding attempts in 1962 and 1963. Several pits in the Lea valley have held breeding populations but the most successful is based on artificial floating islands, purpose-built for the terns, at Rye Meads. In the west of the county breeding was proved for the first time at Stockers Lake (TQ09 L) in 1976.

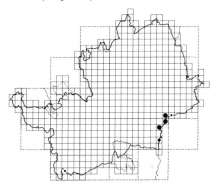

Hertfordshire records from six tetrads			1%
Bedfordshire	2%	Britain & Ireland	23%
London	2%	France (Brittany)	9(35)%
Kent	4%	Netherlands	33%

Hertfordshire status:
Breeding proved in three tetrads (50%) and probable in one more (17%).

This colonial species is now established as a nesting bird on several pits in the Lea valley. A summer visitor it is regularly recorded, particularly at the large pits and reservoirs, on passage in spring and autumn.

STOCK DOVE

Columba oenas

Hertfordshire records from
344 tetrads   68%
Bedfordshire   57%
London   38%
Kent   33%
Britain & Ireland   65%
France (Brittany) 49(51)%
Netherlands   74%

Hertfordshire status:
Breeding proved in 82 tetrads (24%) and probable in 129 more (38%).

A widespread resident bird mainly found in wooded areas. Winter flocks are probably of local origin.

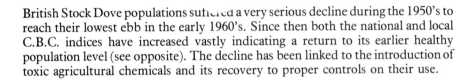

British Stock Dove populations suffered a very serious decline during the 1950's to reach their lowest ebb in the early 1960's. Since then both the national and local C.B.C. indices have increased vastly indicating a return to its earlier healthy population level (see opposite). The decline has been linked to the introduction of toxic agricultural chemicals and its recovery to proper controls on their use.

WOODPIGEON

Columba palumbus

Hertfordshire records from
503 tetrads   100%
Bedfordshire   100%
London   95%
Kent   88%
Britain & Ireland   92%
France (Brittany) 88(95)%
Netherlands   97%

Hertfordshire status:
Breeding proved in 359 tetrads (71%) and probable in 84 more (17%).

Abundant and ubiquitous throughout the year. The winter flocks may cause serious damage to agriculture.

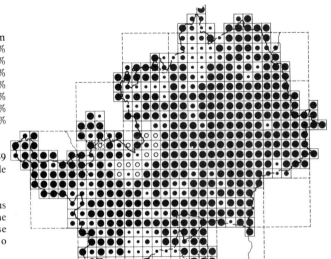

COLLARED DOVE

Streptopelia decaocto

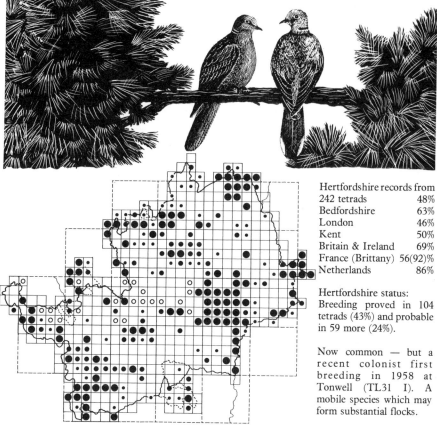

Hertfordshire records from
242 tetrads   48%
Bedfordshire   63%
London   46%
Kent   50%
Britain & Ireland   69%
France (Brittany) 56(92)%
Netherlands   86%

Hertfordshire status:
Breeding proved in 104
tetrads (43%) and probable
in 59 more (24%).

Now common — but a
recent colonist first
breeding in 1958 at
Tonwell (TL31 I). A
mobile species which may
form substantial flocks.

The tremendous increase in the C.B.C. index sums up the Collared Dove's success story. There are now many more birds than the Atlas map shows although, surprisingly, there are still some areas where it does not regularly breed. At least in the initial stages it favoured suburban and even urban areas.

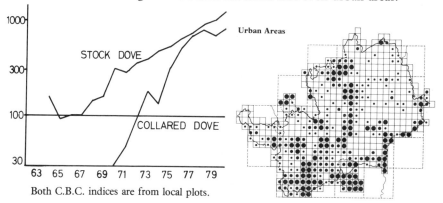

Both C.B.C. indices are from local plots.

51

TURTLE DOVE

Streptopelia turtur

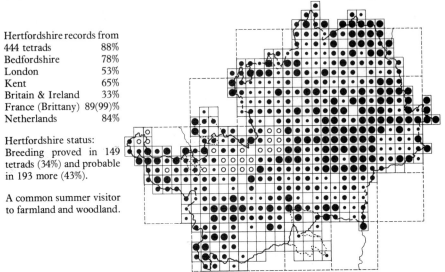

Hertfordshire records from
444 tetrads   88%
Bedfordshire   78%
London   53%
Kent   65%
Britain & Ireland   33%
France (Brittany) 89(99)%
Netherlands   84%

Hertfordshire status:
Breeding proved in 149 tetrads (34%) and probable in 193 more (43%).

A common summer visitor to farmland and woodland.

To many people the soft, purring song of the Turtle Dove is the very sound of summer. A full-scale trans-Saharan migrant which does not return until early May this species may be found nesting in woodland, scrub, copses and along well-grown hedgerows almost anywhere in the county. It is rather susceptible to disturbance and does not nest successfully in urban or suburban areas — as a comparison of the species map with urban development (see below) shows. Both the national and local C.B.C. indices show a fairly steady increase over the last 20 years. Indeed the local population seems to be increasing faster than the national one — not really surprising as Hertfordshire is in the core of its British range whilst some of the plots contributing to the national figures will be from peripheral areas in the north and west of Britain. Ringing of British birds has shown that many pass through Portugal on the autumn passage where, in the past, they were caught and shot in large numbers. It is tempting to relate the population increase in Britain to the legal and actual protection that Turtle Doves are now afforded in Portugal.

Urban Areas

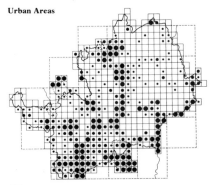

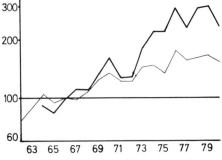

Thick line: local C.B.C., thin line national (all plots)

CUCKOO

Cuculus canorus

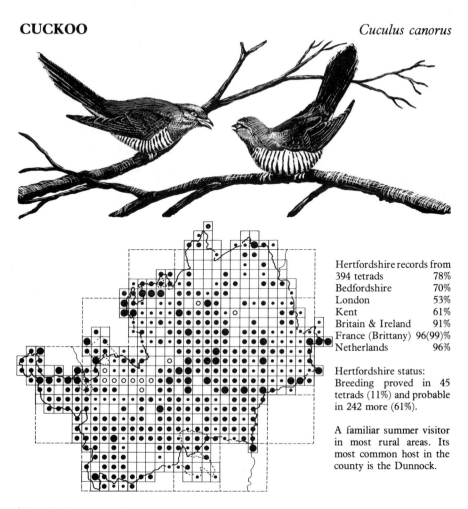

Hertfordshire records from
394 tetrads	78%
Bedfordshire	70%
London	53%
Kent	61%
Britain & Ireland	91%
France (Brittany)	96(99)%
Netherlands	96%

Hertfordshire status:
Breeding proved in 45 tetrads (11%) and probable in 242 more (61%).

A familiar summer visitor in most rural areas. Its most common host in the county is the Dunnock.

The Cuckoo remains well distributed as a breeding species over most of the county. The most notable gaps are either in areas which are built-up (see map opposite) or in the northeast of the county. Here there are very large fields with rather sparse cover, and it may be difficult for the females to find sufficient nests of suitable host species. Apart from Dunnocks the other main foster species is the Reed Warbler where these have strong colonies. The C.B.C. results, both locally and nationally, show a fairly steady population increase over the last 15 years. Many birdwatchers feel that it has actually decreased but this may possibly be a subjective and personal judgement much influenced by local changes due to gradual urbanisation.

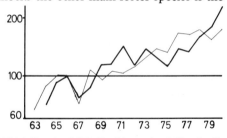

Thick line: local C.B.C., thin: national (farmland).

53

BARN OWL

Tyto alba

Hertfordshire records from

107 tetrads	21%
Bedfordshire	22%
London	13%
Kent	11%
Britain & Ireland	59%
France (Brittany)	67(82)%
Netherlands	42%

Hertfordshire status:
Breeding proved in 33 tetrads (31%) and probable in 26 more (24%).

A scarce resident species absent from many areas but not easy to survey. Young birds disperse during the autumn.

Until the 1940's the 'White Owl' was a familiar bird over most of the county with breeding birds in many farm buildings and holes in trees. Unfortunately a steady and drastic decline then set in which was related to the use of organo-chlorine insecticides. The bodies of Barn Owls sent for analysis often contained very high levels of such chemicals as Aldrin, Dieldrin and D.D.T. During the Atlas period the birds were just beginning to recover and we were very pleased to receive so many records. The main band of positive tetrads broadly follows the most wooded part of the county where it is possible that territories existed which may have been largely unaffected by chemicals. The pattern of records suggests the presence of either small groups of breeding pairs or, just possibly, mobile pairs nesting in slightly different places in successive years. Although a well-known species it was very difficult to record since, if one did not happen to see a flying bird hunting, its presence could easily remain undetected even in a tetrad which was regularly visited. The breeding pair in SP91 G was within 800 metres of the B.T.O. HQ and only found when the young were six weeks old!

54

LITTLE OWL   *Athene noctua*

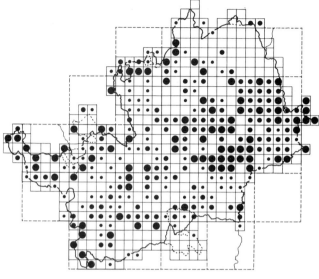

Hertfordshire records from
285 tetrads	57%
Bedfordshire	41%
London	32%
Kent	39%
Britain & Ireland	36%
France (Brittany)	74(88)%
Netherlands	65%

Hertfordshire status:
Breeding proved in 85
tetrads (30%) and probable
in 104 more (36%).

Resident in areas of open
farm and parkland the
Little Owl became
established after intro-
ductions 90 years ago.

The first breeding record in Hertfordshire of the Little Owl was at Easneye in 1897. These birds may have resulted from an introduction in Essex a few years earlier. The main introduction was conducted by Lord Lilford using Dutch birds in Northamptonshire. It took place between 1888 and 1890 and probably resulted in the gradual colonisation of the north of the county from about 1906. By the 1920's it was common over most of Hertfordshire although, within the next decade, its numbers were said to have declined markedly in some areas of the north and west. In common with the rest of England there was a fairly sharp decline from about 1955 to 1965. This was probably related to pesticide usage and happily was reversed so that, for the last 15 years the national C.B.C. index, whilst fluctuating, has shown a slight increase: the best year (1980) having a population level almost double the worst (1963). Local plots held too few birds to calculate a meaningful index but do seem to indicate, if anything, a better rate of increase than nationally. Some recent work in the Berkhamsted area indicates that territorial birds may be very thick on the ground.

TAWNY OWL

Strix aluco

Hertfordshire records from
372 tetrads	74%
Bedfordshire	57%
London	63%
Kent	33%
Britain & Ireland	60%
France (Brittany)	81(91)%
Netherlands	37%

Hertfordshire status:
Breeding proved in 107 tetrads (29%) and probable in 160 more (43%).

Resident in rural, suburban and urban areas wherever there are large trees.

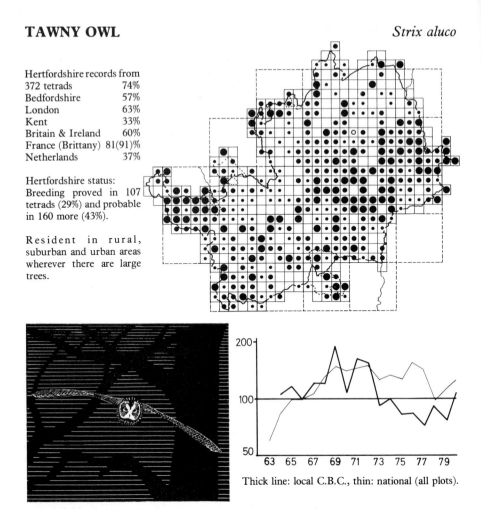

Thick line: local C.B.C., thin: national (all plots).

The Tawny Owl is undoubtedly the commonest owl in the county and its call is a familiar sound in the early spring even in some town centres. The majority of the areas shown as blank on the map are either where there are very large arable fields with little cover and few trees for nesting or built-up areas equally lacking in trees. The territory-holding adult Tawnies are very conservative indeed and the same birds remain in the territory throughout their lives. It seems that local knowledge built up over the years is of very great survival value. During the Atlas fieldwork hooting territorial birds, column 2 records if they persisted, were easily recorded in the spring and, during the summer, proof of breeding could readily be obtained by hearing the characteristic begging calls of the fledged young still dependent on their parents. We think, from the comments of observers on their record cards, that coverage of the county at night for owls was fairly thorough. The national C.B.C. index shows a gradual recovery following the cold winters of 1962-63: the local index is based on rather small samples but may indicate a slight decline during the 1970's.

LONG-EARED OWL   *Asio otus*

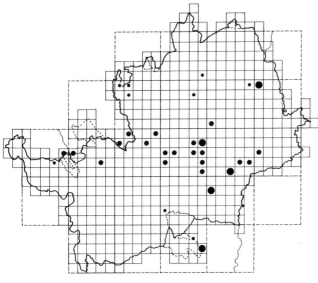

Hertfordshire records from
33 tetrads   7%
Bedfordshire   4%
London   2%
Kent   1%
Britain & Ireland   24%
France (Brittany) 47(33)%
Netherlands   85%

Hertfordshire status:
Breeding proved in five
tetrads (15%) and probable
in 19 more (58%).

Scarce resident mostly in
woods with conifers. In
winter communal roosts
may largely contain
immigrants.

The Long-eared Owl is rather patchily distributed in southeastern England although in Ireland it is locally fairly common — Tawny Owls do not breed there at all. In Hertfordshire many of the birds were found in small conifer plantations where they often nest. The sitting female on an old Carrion Crow's nest often takes a lot of shifting but, later in the season, the grating 'rusty gate' begging call of the young may provide proof of breeding. The majority of the 'column 2' records were of calling birds making the characteristic triple 'Hoo'. One of the more inspired tips for the dedicated Atlas fieldworker was the instruction to carry a half-filled split-sized mineral water bottle on nocturnal expeditions — remove the cap and blow sharply across the bottle to produce the correct note for calling up a Long-eared Owl! In the past the species was thought to be fairly common in Hertfordshire and the sprinkling of 'Hoo Woods' was taken to indicate traditional nesting places. If this was the case then it has certainly declined over the past few decades although Hertfordshire still had more records than the other counties which have produced tetrad atlases.

Woodland

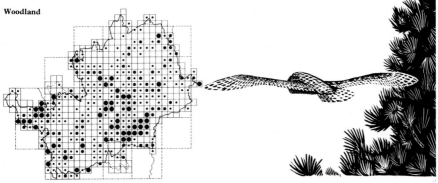

57

NIGHTJAR

Caprimulgus europaeus

Hertfordshire records from

29 tetrads	6%
Bedfordshire	6%
London	4%
Kent	7%
Britain & Ireland	17%
France (Brittany)	45(45)%
Netherlands	15%

Hertfordshire status: Breeding proved in four tetrads (14%) and probable in 17 more (59%).

A summer visitor to areas of heath and young conifer plantations. Formerly common, now scarce and declining.

In Britain the Nightjar is typically a bird of dry lowland heath but, until the turn of the century, it was commonly found breeding in a wide variety of other habitat including downland, dunes and many sorts of open woodland. A steady decline then set in and, over the years, it has become very much reduced in numbers over the whole country. In Hertfordshire it was formerly recorded nesting locally over much more of the county in suitable woodland. Gradually its range became more restricted and many traditional areas were deserted. During the period when conifers were being planted the young trees provided transient but ideal nesting habitat and it was not unusual to find several pairs in a single plantation. At the time of the Atlas fieldwork many plantations were already too well grown to hold Nightjars although the woodland in TL21 and TL30 still held a fair number of pairs. Recent surveys have shown that the decline is continuing and it is unlikely that any have nested in the west of the county for several years. In the east the numbers have been drastically reduced — even from the low level shown on the map.

SWIFT

Apus apus

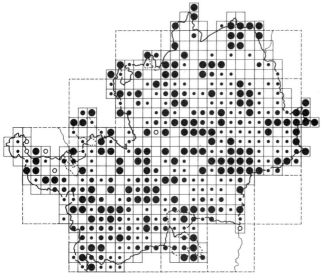

Hertfordshire records from
365 tetrads	72%
Bedfordshire	60%
London	81%
Kent	46%
Britain & Ireland	80%
France (Brittany)	96(98)%
Netherlands	72%

Hertfordshire status:
Breeding proved in 144
tetrads (40%) and probable
in 72 more (20%).

A summer visitor to most
towns and villages. They
may be seen feeding all
over the county from May
to early August.

There are certainly no Swifts breeding in natural sites in Hertfordshire and there can only be a few, at coastal and quarry cliffs, in the whole of Britain. From this it would seem that this species could never have bred in Hertfordshire before man started building. However, on the Continent, particularly in eastern Europe, there are many areas where Swifts regularly nest in holes in trees and it is likely that this used to happen in Britain. Nowadays the normal site is in an older building such as a church tower, the ventilators of the town hall or under the roof of a Victorian villa. As old town centres have been developed such sites have disappeared. In some country areas substantial colonies occur under the old pantile roofs which often allow the birds direct access to a large roof space: in recent years many of these old tiles have been replaced by more modern materials which have excluded the Swifts. It is hoped that the provision of nest boxes, built into existing buildings and new developments, will enable us to retain thriving populations of this interesting species.

Urban Areas

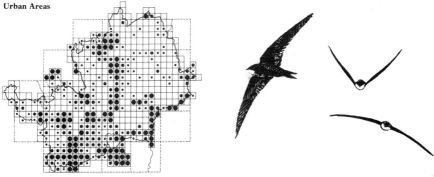

59

KINGFISHER

Alcedo atthis

Hertfordshire records from
95 tetrads   19%
Bedfordshire   22%
London   16%
Kent   11%
Britain & Ireland   47%
France (Brittany) 56(91)%
Netherlands   25%

Hertfordshire status:
Breeding proved in 44
tetrads (46%) and probable
in 19 more (20%).

Regularly recorded on
most waters but breeding
birds need a vertical face
for the nest. Badly affected
by severe winters.

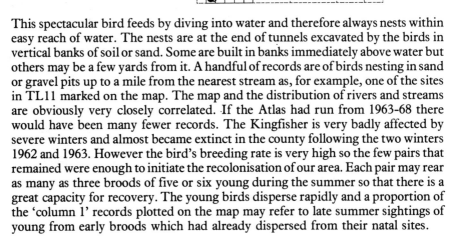

This spectacular bird feeds by diving into water and therefore always nests within easy reach of water. The nests are at the end of tunnels excavated by the birds in vertical banks of soil or sand. Some are built in banks immediately above water but others may be a few yards from it. A handful of records are of birds nesting in sand or gravel pits up to a mile from the nearest stream as, for example, one of the sites in TL11 marked on the map. The map and the distribution of rivers and streams are obviously very closely correlated. If the Atlas had run from 1963-68 there would have been many fewer records. The Kingfisher is very badly affected by severe winters and almost became extinct in the county following the two winters 1962 and 1963. However the bird's breeding rate is very high so the few pairs that remained were enough to initiate the recolonisation of our area. Each pair may rear as many as three broods of five or six young during the summer so that there is a great capacity for recovery. The young birds disperse rapidly and a proportion of the 'column 1' records plotted on the map may refer to late summer sightings of young from early broods which had already dispersed from their natal sites.

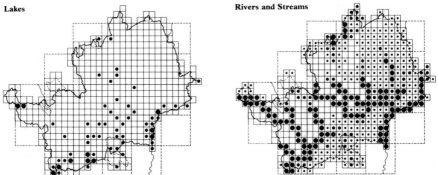

Lakes

Rivers and Streams

WRYNECK

Jynx torquilla

Hertfordshire records from four tetrads   1%
Bedfordshire   -%   Britain & Ireland   1%
London   2%   France (Brittany)   51(25)%
Kent   1%   Netherlands   8%

Hertfordshire status:
Breeding proved in one tetrad (25%) and probable in one more (25%).

Formerly a widespread breeding species, now only irregularly recorded in the summer. In the 1970's the only nesting records were during 1972, 1973 and 1977. Most Wrynecks are now seen in the county during the autumn passage when Continental birds are often recorded.

The sad decline of this primitive woodpecker, a trans-Saharan migrant, has not been confined to Hertfordshire for it used to be a common summer visitor over the whole of southeast England. The maps below show how its British distribution has dwindled over the last two thirds of a century. This has affected the whole of its western European range and there seems to be little chance of it returning to Hertfordshire to breed in any numbers. The four Hertfordshire Atlas records were from a traditional site in TL31, where breeding was proved, from TL01 where a territorial bird was found in one year and from TQ09 and TL20 where there were 'column 1' records.

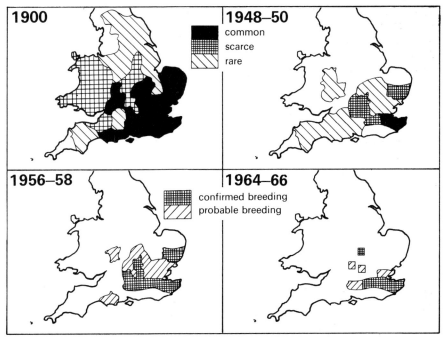

The distribution of Wrynecks in southern Britain for 1900, 1948-50, 1956-58 and 1964-66. The black areas shown in the top two maps had Wrynecks commonly breeding, cross-hatched had proved breeding birds and diagonal hatching suspected breeding.

61

GREEN WOODPECKER   *Picus viridis*

Hertfordshire records from
197 tetrads	39%
Bedfordshire	32%
London	25%
Kent	37%
Britain & Ireland	42%
France (Brittany)	92(93)%
Netherlands	50%

Hertfordshire status:
Breeding proved in 49
tetrads (25%) and probable
in 78 more (40%).

A patchily distributed
resident species of park and
grassland with trees for
nesting.

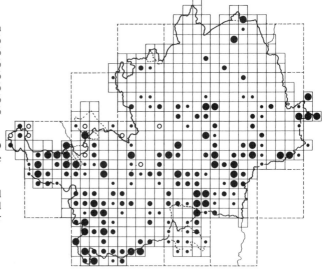

Woodland

Although Green Woodpeckers need trees
in which to excavate their breeding holes
they are not dependent on trees for their
food. Indeed they are most commonly
seen feeding at ant hills in grassland
areas: they use their sticky tongue to
harvest the ants from the galleries of their
nests. They are badly hit by severe
weather and the national C.B.C. index
shows the recovery after 1962-63
continuing until 1966 or 1967. The
population has been stable since that time.

GREAT SPOTTED WOODPECKER — *Dendrocopos major*

Hertfordshire records from	
224 tetrads	44%
Bedfordshire	32%
London	48%
Kent	31%
Britain & Ireland	53%
France (Brittany)	90(91)%
Netherlands	70%

Hertfordshire status:
Breeding proved in 70 tetrads (31%) and probable in 79 more (35%).

A common resident of most larger areas of woodland. Little evidence of movement but may visit bird-tables in winter.

LESSER SPOTTED WOODPECKER — *Dendrocopos minor*

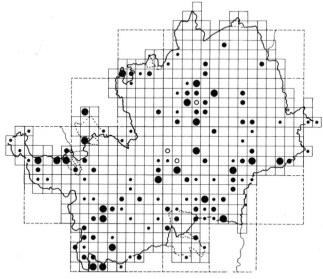

Hertfordshire records from	
128 tetrads	25%
Bedfordshire	20%
London	27%
Kent	9%
Britain & Ireland	23%
France (Brittany)	55(82)%
Netherlands	29%

Hertfordshire status:
Breeding proved in 23 tetrads (18%) and probable in 50 more (39%).

A widely distributed but easily overlooked resident of woodland.

Few major areas of woodland are without this species although, as the figures show, it is not so widely distributed as the Great Spotted. In many areas with mature trees the Great Spotted is readily recorded for it may be quite conspicuous but the smaller species may remain in the canopy, unseen from below. Many of the Atlas recorders were only able to locate the Lessers because of their characteristic calls.

WOODLARK

Lullula arborea

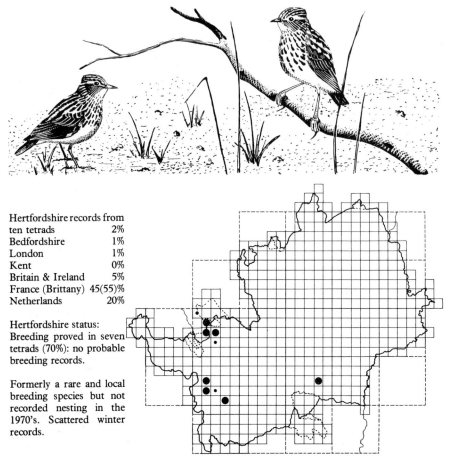

Hertfordshire records from	
ten tetrads	2%
Bedfordshire	1%
London	1%
Kent	0%
Britain & Ireland	5%
France (Brittany)	45(55)%
Netherlands	20%

Hertfordshire status:
Breeding proved in seven tetrads (70%): no probable breeding records.

Formerly a rare and local breeding species but not recorded nesting in the 1970's. Scattered winter records.

The Woodlark has probably never been at all common in Hertfordshire but, over the last few decades, the breeding population has dwindled to extinction. This is in line with the marked fluctuations in the total British breeding population which was probably at its peak in the 1940's and then declined dramatically until a few years ago. There is now every reason to expect a gradual increase in Britain during which the species should return to breed in Hertfordshire in small numbers. The habitat favoured by the Woodlark, open scrubby grass or heathland with scattered trees, still exists in several places. The song is distinctive with some particularly rich fruity notes. Unfortunately, in the past the much more widespread Tree Pipit has frequently been mistaken by inexperienced birdwatchers for the Woodlark — indeed its country name, Titlark, partly suggests this. There are, however, no grounds for attributing any of the more recently published records to such mistakes. One can only hope that it makes a good recovery to allow local birdwatchers the opportunity of hearing its beautiful song.

SKYLARK   *Alauda arvensis*

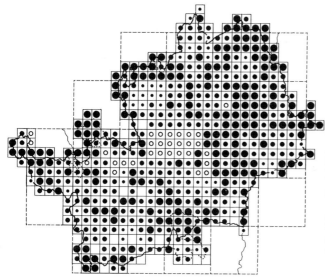

Hertfordshire records from
494 tetrads   98%
Bedfordshire   99%
London   77%
Kent   85%
Britain & Ireland   98%
France (Brittany)
                  91(100)%
Netherlands   98%

Hertfordshire status:
Breeding proved in 200
tetrads (40%) and probable
in 224 more (45%).

An abundant and resident
breeding species of all
agricultural areas. Some
winter movement.

The Skylark was recorded in almost every tetrad not completely covered by urban or suburban development. They are probably at their densest along the Chilterns on chalk grasslands where dozens of singing birds may be within earshot at once. Although they happily breed in the middle of huge, featureless fields they are equally at home in small fields bordered by hedges. Grassy areas in water meadows, gravel pits and even roadside verges may hold good populations. There is some evidence, from detailed census work, that the densest breeding groups are found on well-grazed permanent pasture but even areas of arable land can support healthy populations. The C.B.C. graphs show both the national and local indices recovering from the effects of the 1962-63 cold winters. Skylarks are often very quick to move out in bad weather but it seems that the local populations fared particularly badly in the hard winters. The local index subsequently increased at a higher rate than the national one. It is possible that the increasingly intensive cultivation of the county may have helped the Skylark to thrive.

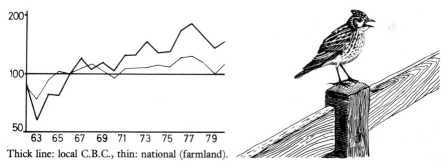

Thick line: local C.B.C., thin: national (farmland).

65

SAND MARTIN

Riparia riparia

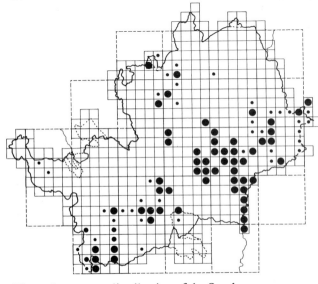

Hertfordshire records from
98 tetrads   19%
Bedfordshire   17%
London   21%
Kent   11%
Britain & Ireland   75%
France (Brittany) 40(86)%
Netherlands   36%

Hertfordshire status:
Breeding proved in 56
tetrads (57%) and probable
in four more (4%).

Colonial breeding species
in sand and gravel pits.
Passage birds often seen
over water even at mid-
summer.

The rather sparse distribution of the Sand Martin as a breeding species in Hertfordshire reflects the lack of suitable sand or gravel faces for the bird to excavate its nesting hole. These are only available where man has extracted sand or gravel leaving vertical edges to the pit. In a very few cases soil over chalk or clay has been used and there are records of birds nesting in drainage pipes. During the winter of 1968/69 Sand Martins suffered a disaster on their wintering grounds — probably associated with the Sahelian drought — and, the following summer, their British breeding population dropped by about 70%.

Gravel deposits

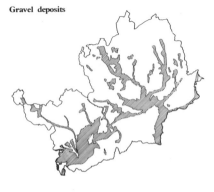

SWALLOW

Hirundo rustica

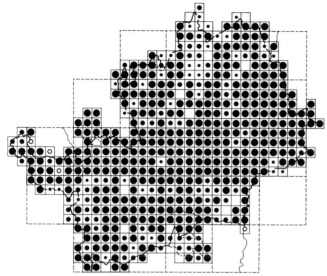

Hertfordshire records from
488 tetrads	97%
Bedfordshire	89%
London	78%
Kent	87%
Britain & Ireland	93%
France (Brittany)	
	98(100)%
Netherlands	95%

Hertfordshire status:
Breeding proved in 376 tetrads (77%) and probable in 71 more (15%).

A familiar summer visitor nesting on and in buildings in rural and suburban areas. Local C.B.C. index currently higher than during the Atlas period.

HOUSE MARTIN

Delichon urbica

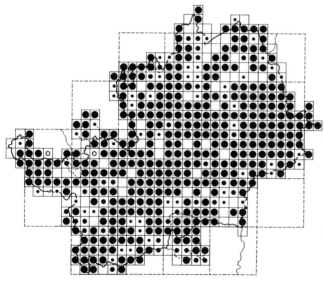

Hertfordshire records from
444 tetrads	88%
Bedfordshire	68%
London	84%
Kent	69%
Britain & Ireland	86%
France (Brittany)	98(98)%
Netherlands	93%

Hertfordshire status:
Breeding proved in 357 tetrads (80%) and probable in 35 more (8%).

A familiar summer visitor nesting colonially on the outside of buildings or under bridges.

Both House Martin and Swallows depend on supplies of mud for nest-building. This may be delayed for some weeks in years when there has been a drought in early summer and mud is not available at river or stream sides. Unlike the Swallows, House Martins often breed in towns and may readily colonise newly built houses on modern estates. Well established colonies may include 20 of more pairs.

TREE PIPIT

Anthus trivialis

Hertfordshire records from
141 tetrads   28%
Bedfordshire   14%
London   22%
Kent   17%
Britain & Ireland 46%
France (Brittany) 82(83)%
Netherlands   54%

Hertfordshire status:
Breeding proved in 46
tetrads (33%) and probable
in 76 more (54%).

A summer visitor to
woodland clearings and
areas of scrub.

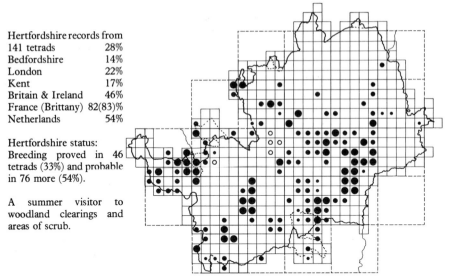

The Tree Pipit is a common summer visitor in most of the major woodland areas of Hertfordshire. If anything it is probably less common to the north and east of the county — the National Atlas shows that it is not common in the adjacent parts of Cambridge and Essex. It is typically found breeding in the clearings of deciduous woodland, sometimes even along broad rides, and in well grown scrub. It is sometimes abundant in newly planted conifer areas but generally only where a few taller trees have been left to nurse the crop. These tall trees are needed by the territorial birds as song posts from which they can launch into their characteristic song-flights. Their distinctive songs and different display flights helped Atlas workers to distinguish the similar Tree and Meadow Pipits even in the few tetrads, generally along the Chiltern scarp, where both bred. The national C.B.C. index (see opposite) for Tree Pipit shows a slight decline over the last ten years or so. There were not enough birds on the local plots to calculate a local index but it seems likely that the Hertfordshire population has followed the national trends.

Woodland

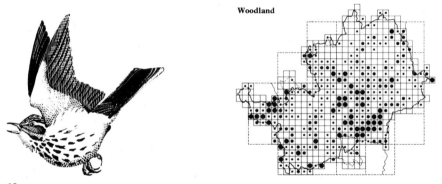

MEADOW PIPIT   *Anthus pratensis*

Hertfordshire records from
107 tetrads   21%
Bedfordshire   22%
London   23%
Kent   30%
Britain & Ireland   94%
France (Brittany) 33(95)%
Netherlands   94%

Hertfordshire status:
Breeding proved in 42
tetrads (39%) and probable
in 18 more (17%).

A   sparsely   distributed
breeding bird of chalk
grassland and wet meadow
areas.   Widespread   on
passage and in the winter.

The Meadow Pipit is a bird of open areas of grassland. In Hertfordshire there are
two different areas where they may be found breeding — the chalk grassland along
the Chiltern scarp and the wet meadows of the Colne and Lea. In other parts of the
county pairs may sometimes be found on permanent pasture or sometimes in dry
gravel pits. These areas have probably always held Meadow Pipits but, over the
last few decades, there must be many areas on the chalk which have been ploughed
and water meadows that have been drained which have lost their Meadow Pipits.
The other three counties to have published tetrad maps all had slightly more
Meadow Pipit records than Hertfordshire. The preferred habitats in Bedfordshire
and Hertfordshire were similar whilst in London the main areas were the Thames
valley and the Surrey heaths and in Kent downland and, more commonly, coastal
areas were used. The national C.B.C. index, shown below, has fluctuated over the
last decade having probably taken a few years to recover from cold winter losses.
There are too few birds on local plots for a local index to be calculated.

Altitude

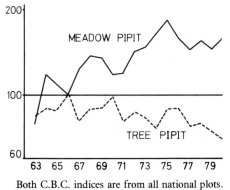

Both C.B.C. indices are from all national plots.

YELLOW WAGTAIL

Motacilla flava

Hertfordshire records from
57 tetrads	11%
Bedfordshire	23%
London	18%
Kent	28%
Britain & Ireland	30%
France (Brittany)	44(68)%
Netherlands	85%

Hertfordshire status:
Breeding proved in 28 tetrads (49%) and probable in 14 more (25%).

Local summer visitor to water meadows, gravel pits and the Gault Clay area north of Tring. More widely recorded on passage.

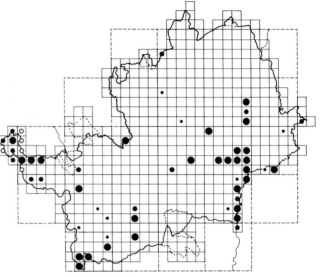

GREY WAGTAIL

Motacilla cinerea

Hertfordshire records from
55 tetrads	11%
Bedfordshire	4%
London	13%
Kent	6%
Britain & Ireland	71%
France (Brittany)	61(77)%
Netherlands	5%

Hertfordshire status:
Breeding proved in 40 tetrads (73%) and probable in six more (11%).

As a nesting bird found beside fast-flowing water. Winter and passage records from other areas.

Primarily a bird of rushing upland streams the Grey Wagtail is very adept at finding suitable breeding sites in our lowland county. In the east it is often found breeding beside the weirs on the rivers and streams of the Lea catchment. Other sites include the sluices at sewage farms, overflow streams at gravel pits and locks along the canals. The population is currently high but may be reduced after severe winters.

70

PIED WAGTAIL   *Motacilla alba*

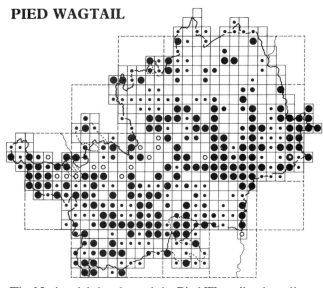

Hertfordshire records from
344 tetrads   68%
Bedfordshire   64%
London   76%
Kent   55%
Britain & Ireland   94%
France (Brittany) 88(93)%
Netherlands   98%

Hertfordshire status:
Breeding proved in 160
tetrads (47%) and probable
in 53 more (15%).

Widely distributed as a
breeding bird except in the
driest areas. Many winter
immigrants.

The National Atlas showed the Pied Wagtail as breeding over the whole mainland of Britain and Ireland. It may therefore seem a little surprising that the tetrad map for Hertfordshire should show so many 'holes'. Many of those in the north of the county are for tetrads which probably contained hardly any buildings — the most usual nest-site. In the south and central areas some of the gaps might normally be expected to have held breeding Pied Wagtails but, as the local C.B.C. index shows, the recovery in Hertfordshire following the disastrous losses over 1962-63 was much slower than nationally. Most of the proved records came from tetrads with some water in them, the slow recovery of the Pied Wagtail in Hertfordshire may possibly be attributed to the overall dryness of the county.

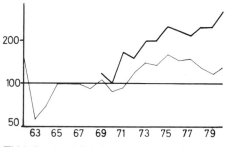
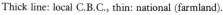

Thick line: local C.B.C., thin: national (farmland).

Rivers and Streams

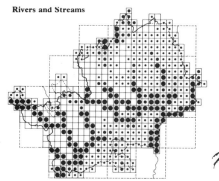

71

WREN

Troglodytes troglodytes

Hertfordshire records from
499 tetrads	99%
Bedfordshire	100%
London	96%
Kent	87%
Britain & Ireland	97%
France (Brittany)	
	97(100)%
Netherlands	96%

Hertfordshire status:
Breeding proved in 295
tetrads (59%) and probable
in 150 more (30%).

Abundant resident in all
areas with thick cover for
its concealment.

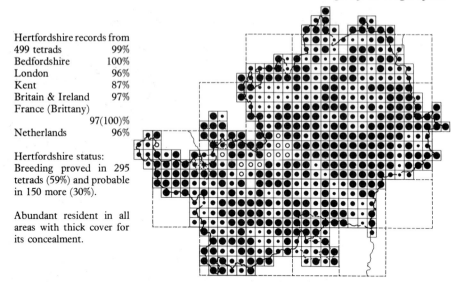

There were only five tetrads in Hertfordshire without Wrens. Nationally only Skylark and Carrion Crow were more widespread in Britain and it is most likely that every Hertfordshire tetrad actually held breeding pairs — at least by the end of the Atlas period. This tiny bird has very small nesting territories which may be in gardens, along hedges or in the very smallest copse or wood. Probably the densest populations are found in woodland, deciduous or coniferous, with a thick ground layer. Such sites on the Ashridge Estate, dominated by planted conifers or natural Birch, may often have a breeding pair every hectare. This is, of course, only true when the population is at a high level. The C.B.C. indices (see below) both show the same 1963 minimum of 31. The maximum, in both cases during 1975, was 351 nationally and 304 locally. These huge increases show how well this vulnerable little bird can recover from the depredations of severe winter weather. Given good summer weather a pair might rear three broods totalling 15 young.

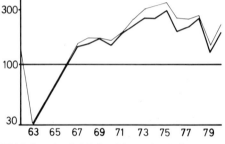

Thick line: local C.B.C., thin: national (farmland).

DUNNOCK
Prunella modularis

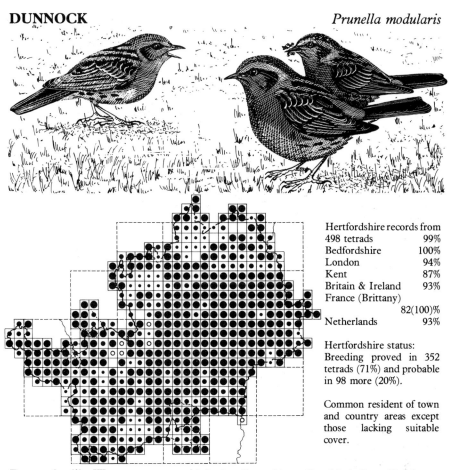

Hertfordshire records from
498 tetrads	99%
Bedfordshire	100%
London	94%
Kent	87%
Britain & Ireland	93%
France (Brittany)	82(100)%
Netherlands	93%

Hertfordshire status:
Breeding proved in 352 tetrads (71%) and probable in 98 more (20%).

Common resident of town and country areas except those lacking suitable cover.

Dunnocks, like Wrens, are very widely distributed breeding birds found in almost any form of cover. The map shows many more proved breeding records than that for Wren, probably because, as the C.B.C. index shows, the Dunnock had recovered from the 1962 and 1963 winters well before the Atlas fieldwork began. Over the last 15 years the population has remained very steady both nationally and locally. Several of the six blank tetrads, like those for Wren, also show up as being rather poorly recorded (see page 121). This is actually one of the few maps showing the distribution of one species which is of great importance to another; in Hertfordshire many Dunnocks are hosts to Cuckoos. Up to 3% of the Dunnocks that rear young rear a Cuckoo and not a brood of baby Dunnocks.

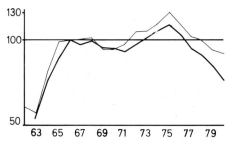

Thick line: local C.B.C., thin: national (farmland).

73

ROBIN

Erithacus rubecula

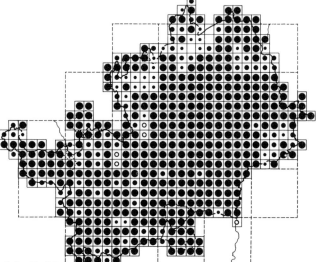

Hertfordshire records from
501 tetrads	99%
Bedfordshire	100%
London	93%
Kent	84%
Britain & Ireland	93%
France (Brittany)	96(99)%
Netherlands	85%

Hertfordshire status:
Breeding proved in 399
tetrads (80%) and probable
in 68 more (14%).

Abundant and ubiquitous
resident. Some move away
during the winter but most
remain.

A very high proportion of the Robin records were of proved breeding. This is probably because of the distinctive juvenile plumage and conspicuous begging behaviour by the newly fledged youngsters. The sparser areas, in the northern part of the county, are very open with rather little cover for breeding Robins although, even here, most tetrads would certainly hold at least a pair or two. The Robin and Dunnock C.B.C. indices are very similar and it is unlikely that the short-term effects of the 1962-63 winters on Robin populations will have influenced the distribution.

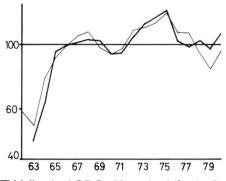

Thick line: local C.B.C., thin: national (farmland).

74

NIGHTINGALE

Luscinia megarhynchos

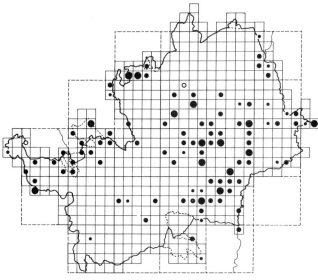

Hertfordshire records from
100 tetrads	20%
Bedfordshire	17%
London	10%
Kent	37%
Britain & Ireland	17%
France (Brittany)	82(31)%
Netherlands	55%

Hertfordshire status:
Breeding proved in 15
tetrads (15%) and probable
in 66 more (66%).

Scarce and declining
summer visitor to wood-
land areas with thick cover.

The Nightingale was considered by Bryan Sage, writing in the late 1950's, to be 'a fairly common summer visitor to most areas'. The tetrad map shows a fairly wide distribution of singing birds (breeding is very difficult to prove for this species). The records are centred on the main woodland areas (see map below) although there are five records in the southwestern four 10-km squares. The preferred habitat is rather specialised with tall trees, dense thickets and a rich ground flora. This is best obtained through the traditional 'coppice with standards' management which has all but ceased in the county. The Atlas records undoubtedly represent a marked decline since the 1950's — Sage reported many more including about 100 singing males in the extensive woodland block shared by TL30 and TL31. The situation since the Atlas has become critical. In 1980 the B.T.O. organised a Nightingale survey and Brian Sawford's map of the species in Hertfordshire tells its own story. The grand total of birds recorded was only 21 and there were reports from a tenth of the tetrads in which Nightingales were found over the period 1967-73.

Semi-natural Woodland

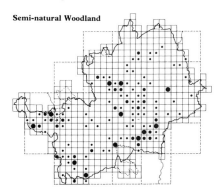

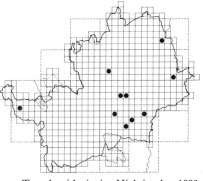

Tetrads with singing Nightingales: 1980

75

BLACK REDSTART

Phoenicurus ochruros

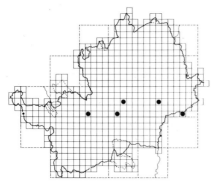

Hertfordshire records from seven tetrads 1%
Bedfordshire 1% Britain & Ireland 2%
London 5% France (Brittany) 86(69)%
Kent 1% Netherlands 63%

Hertfordshire status:
Breeding proved in six tetrads (86%): no probable breeding records.

Scattered breeding records: currently probably annually. Industrial, urban and rural sites have been used but always with extensive buildings — factory, gravel cleaning plant, railway station and large farmyard for example. Some records on passage and a very few in winter.

REDSTART

Phoenicurus phoenicurus

Hertfordshire records from
49 tetrads 10%
Bedfordshire 8%
London 8%
Kent 4%
Britain & Ireland 43%
France (Brittany) 73(53)%
Netherlands 76%

Hertfordshire status:
Breeding proved in 14 tetrads (29%) and probable in 12 more (24%).

Scarce summer visitor to areas of ancient woodland. Passage migrants common in autumn.

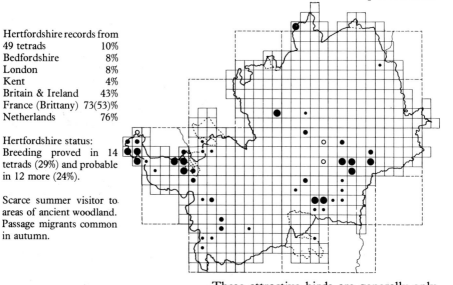

Semi-natural Woodland

These attractive birds are generally only found in established deciduous woodland. The population on the Gault Clay northwest of Tring were breeding in mature hedgerows but have now died out. In a few areas pairs have been found breeding in wet carr-like scrub. Redstart populations fell due to the Sahelian drought affecting the ecology of their winter quarters. At its worst the British C.B.C. index fell to 23 (1973) but more recently it has increased and reached 90 in 1980 — its highest level since 100 in 1967.

WHINCHAT   *Saxicola rubetra*

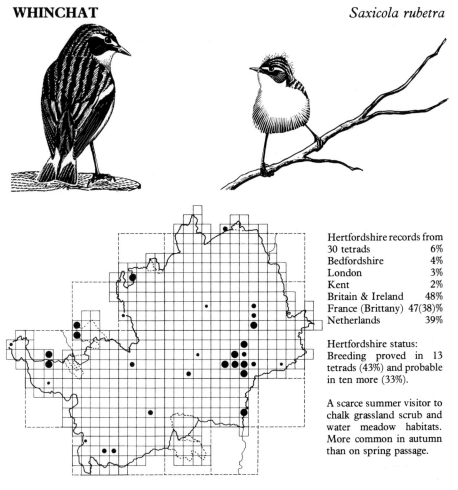

Hertfordshire records from
30 tetrads	6%
Bedfordshire	4%
London	3%
Kent	2%
Britain & Ireland	48%
France (Brittany)	47(38)%
Netherlands	39%

Hertfordshire status:
Breeding proved in 13
tetrads (43%) and probable
in ten more (33%).

A scarce summer visitor to
chalk grassland scrub and
water meadow habitats.
More common in autumn
than on spring passage.

Whinchats are locally regular breeding birds in two Hertfordshire habitats. The main one is now the water meadow and gravel pit areas of the Lea and its tributaries but there are still some birds breeding along the Chiltern scarp. These latter generally nest on the lower slopes where the grass grows thicker for, in both habitats, they nest in rank, tussocky grass. Generally they use fence posts or small bushes as song perches and they can be spotted from a considerable distance. As long-distance migrants they are fairly regular on passage during both the autumn and spring. It is just possible that the scattered records in other parts of the county are due to spring migrants finding suitable territories (and a mate) and staying in the county to breed. Certainly they are well-known for their habit of arriving to breed in a tiny area of suitable habitat for a single year and then disappearing again. The other southeastern counties to produce tetrad maps have similar striking rates to Hertfordshire and the National Atlas shows that the core area of the Whinchat's distribution in Britain lies north and west of a line from the Humber to the Bristol Channel.

STONECHAT   *Saxicola torquata*

Hertfordshire records from four tetrads		1%
Bedfordshire	1%	Britain & Ireland	52%
London	2%	France (Brittany)	91(100)%
Kent	2%	Netherlands	46%

Hertfordshire status:
Breeding proved in two tetrads (50%): no probable breeding records.

Now scarce and irregular as a breeding species the Stonechat was formerly widely distributed on heaths and commons. Loss of habitat and the effects of severe winters have contributed to the decline. It is still regularly recorded during the winter.

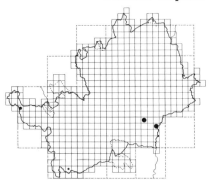

WHEATEAR   *Oenanthe oenanthe*

Hertfordshire records from 14 tetrads		3%
Bedfordshire	3%	Britain & Ireland	62%
London	1%	France (Brittany)	33(43)%
Kent	3%	Netherlands	40%

Hertfordshire status:
Breeding proved in one tetrad (7%) and probable in one more (7%).

Very sporadic breeding summer visitor with nesting records once every ten or twenty years. The record in TL02 Z was actually over the county boundary in Bedfordshire. Widespread on passage in spring and autumn.

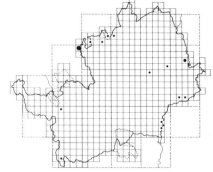

Wheatears have never been common breeding birds in Hertfordshire although, at first sight, the rabbit-infested sheepwalks of the Chiltern scarp would seem to have been ideal habitat. The only area where it was ever found nesting in any numbers was on the hills round Royston. Further south, in Hampshire and Sussex, the downland held substantial breeding populations until the end of the last century but these have now declined.

BLACKBIRD   *Turdus merula*

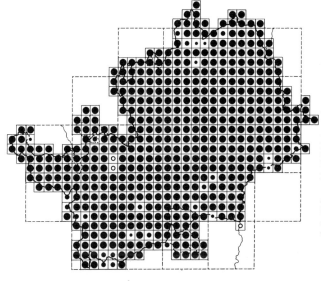

Hertfordshire records from
504 tetrads   100%
Bedfordshire   100%
London   97%
Kent   95%
Britain & Ireland   96%
France (Brittany) 98(99)%
Netherlands   97%

Hertfordshire status:
Breeding proved in 476
tetrads (94%) and probable
in 18 more (4%).

Abundant resident breed-
ing species throughout the
area. Many Continental
visitors in winter.

Breeding Blackbirds may be found throughout the county from the urban areas of the centres of large towns to the open rolling hills south of Royston. Here they are rather sparsely distributed but will nest in the meanest of hedges or even, if all else fails, on the ground sheltered by nettles or other vegetation. Blackbirds were very easy to prove for they have a prolonged breeding season. In most years it starts early in March and, provided the summer is damp, continues to August. In dry summers food, in the form of soil-dwelling invertebrates, becomes much less easy to obtain and breeding may stop, except in damp areas, as early as mid-June. For the dedicated Atlas worker almost all forms of proof of breeding could readily be obtained over a period of up to four or five months. The C.B.C. results show that the national and local indices are very much in step — hardly surprising for the sample, even for the local graph, is very high. The cold weather effects were very quickly redressed and the population, throughout the Atlas period, may have been slightly higher than over the last four summers. The recent slight fall probably shows the effects both of the two very hot years and a couple of fairly cold winters.

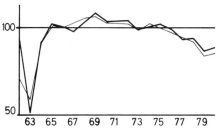

Thick line: local C.B.C., thin: national (farmland).

79

SONG THRUSH   *Turdus philomelos*

Hertfordshire records from
504 tetrads   100%
Bedfordshire   100%
London   96%
Kent   92%
Britain & Ireland   95%
France (Brittany)
                  86(100)%
Netherlands   94%

Hertfordshire status:
Breeding proved in 461
tetrads (91%) and probable
in 30 more (6%).

An extremely common
resident breeding bird.
Evidence of some passage
but few winter immigrants.

Like the Blackbird the Song Thrush is found breeding in every part of the county. It is equally adaptable in its nesting site and the one species may build on the old nest of the other! Both use mud in their nest construction but it is the Song Thrush which lays the very rich blue eggs directly onto the smooth mud lining. There is no direct evidence from Hertfordshire to point to any long-term overall change to the current Blackbird dominance which is general over the whole of Britain. However, nationally, there is evidence that Song Thrush numbers were, before the War, much higher than they are now and they may even have exceeded Blackbirds. The C.B.C. indices, both national and local, are very similar and follow the same sort of pattern as those of the Blackbird. However the Song Thrush, much the smaller species, is undoubtedly more vulnerable to cold weather than the Blackbird, as is clear from the indices following the 1962-63 cold winters, and therefore much more likely to fluctuate in population level. The local C.B.C. appears to be running slightly lower than the national index, this may be an artefact resulting from a quirk during 1966 when both indices were set arbitrarily at 100.

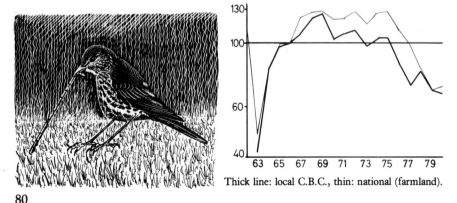

Thick line: local C.B.C., thin: national (farmland).

80

MISTLE THRUSH   *Turdus viscivorus*

Hertfordshire records from
418 tetrads   83%
Bedfordshire   63%
London   86%
Kent   78%
Britain & Ireland 88%
France (Brittany) 80(98)%
Netherlands   76%

Hertfordshire status:
Breeding proved in 255 tetrads (61%) and probable in 74 more (18%).

A common resident bird over most of the county. Flocks may form in the late summer.

The Mistle Thrush is well distributed over most of the county although rather less common than the Blackbird and Song Thrush. The most usual feeding grounds are on grazed grassland or lawns and they are more common in suburban areas and the southern part of the county than the predominantly rural and arable region south of Royston. The Mistle Thrush starts to breed very early with eggs often laid in February but generally has two, even three, broods and so can be recorded by Atlas workers through most of the normal period for fieldwork. The national C.B.C. index shows that the effects of the 1962/63 winter was very marked. This is perhaps surprising for the Mistle Thrush is much the biggest of the three species breeding in Hertfordshire and should therefore be expected to stand the cold better than the others. The main recovery took some three or four years and then the population fluctuated within quite narrow limits. The local index seems to have increased over the last three years but is based on rather few pairs — a maximum of 54 in any year and a minimum of 27.

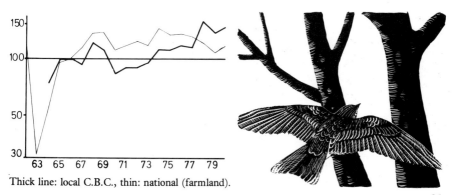

Thick line: local C.B.C., thin: national (farmland).

81

GRASSHOPPER WARBLER

Locustella naevia

Hertfordshire records from
136 tetrads   27%
Bedfordshire   23%
London   15%
Kent   18%
Britain & Ireland   67%
France (Brittany) 35(64)%
Netherlands   34%

Hertfordshire status:
Breeding proved in 23 tetrads (17%) and probable in 102 more (75%).

A regular summer migrant to areas of rank vegetation whether wet or dry. Young conifer plantations are particularly favoured.

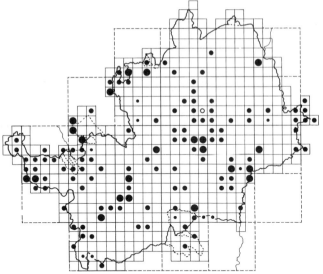

Historical records indicate a general decrease in the county earlier this century but there has been a marked increase over the last twenty years.

SEDGE WARBLER

Acrocephalus schoenobaenus

Hertfordshire records from
209 tetrads   41%
Bedfordshire   36%
London   24%
Kent   27%
Britain & Ireland   76%
France (Brittany) 40(81)%
Netherlands   58%

Hertfordshire status:
Breeding proved in 90 tetrads (43%) and probable in 85 more (41%).

A locally common summer visitor to damp areas of rank vegetation. Common on spring and autumn passage, often in other habitats.

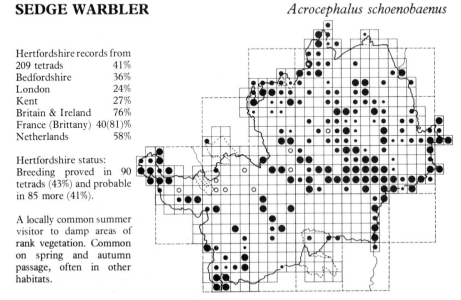

Although most common in damp habitats some Sedge Warblers regularly breed in dry areas. Suitable breeding areas which develop at transient sites (e.g. gravel pits) are quickly colonised. *See C.B.C. indices opposite.*

REED WARBLER

Acrocephalus scirpaceus

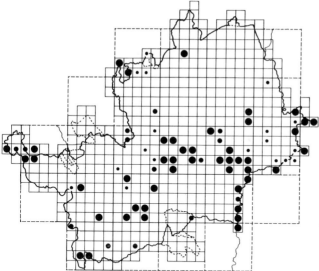

Hertfordshire records from

78 tetrads	15%
Bedfordshire	16%
London	14%
Kent	20%
Britain & Ireland	20%
France (Brittany)	48(68)%
Netherlands	75%

Hertfordshire status:
Breeding proved in 46 tetrads (59%) and probable in 14 more (18%).

A very local summer visitor generally dependent on *Phragmites* reed-beds for breeding.

Phragmites

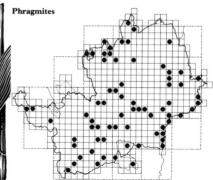

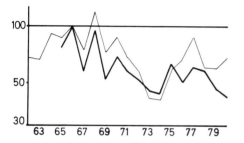

C.B.C. indices for Sedge Warbler. The marked decline in the early 1970's is correlated with the effects of the Sahelian drought on the ecology of its wintering grounds in Africa.

Breeding Reed Warblers are generally colonial and nest in *Phragmites* reed-beds or the vegetation at their edges. The map, redrawn from John Dony's *Flora of Hertfordshire,* shows the distribution of *Phragmites* a few years before the bird Atlas fieldwork. Although this dependence provides the Reed Warblers with an ideal plant for nesting the colonial habit makes then particularly vulnerable to Cuckoo parasitism.

LESSER WHITETHROAT

Sylvia curruca

Hertfordshire records from

244 tetrads	48%
Bedfordshire	45%
London	32%
Kent	31%
Britain & Ireland	28%
France (Brittany)	26(-)%
Netherlands	78%

Hertfordshire status:
Breeding proved in 55
tetrads (23%) and probable
in 125 more (51%).

A fairly widespread and
locally common summer
visitor to scrubland and
hedges. Common on
passage.

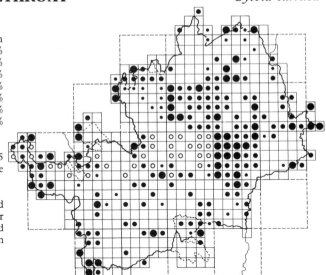

This very attractive little summer visitor is most often found in scrubland, woodland fringe and well-grown hedgerows. It is one of the few migrants to leave Britain southeastwards in the autumn and winters in East Africa. On its arrival in April or early May territorial males have a rather plain, rattling little song which is easily overlooked — not only is it rather nondescript but it is also often uttered for only a few days. Unlike its close relative, the Whitethroat, it does not have a conspicuous song-flight and it is very easily overlooked. These difficulties are probably reflected in the larger proportion of 'column 1' records than for the other three *Sylvia* species. The C.B.C. indices look rather unusual because, for both the local and national graphs, the base year for the index, 1966, happens to have been that with the highest population. A decline in the late 1960's and early 1970's seems to have been at least partly regained. Although they do not move southwards to the Sahel it is possible that the effects of the drought extended far to the east in the sub-Saharan zone.

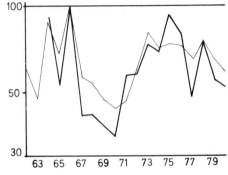

Thick line: local C.B.C., thin: national (farmland).

WHITETHROAT

Sylvia communis

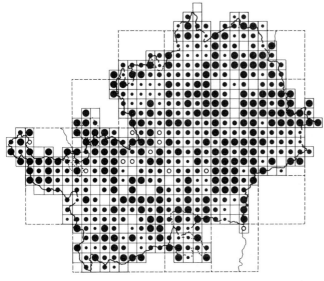

Hertfordshire records from
471 tetrads   93%
Bedfordshire   71%
London   70%
Kent   62%
Britain & Ireland   83%
France (Brittany) 87(99)%
Netherlands   91%

Hertfordshire status:
Breeding proved in 215
tetrads (46%) and probable
in 188 more (40%).

Still a common visitor in
summer to scrub and farm
hedges: numbers much
fewer than before 1969.

The Whitethroat is a widespread and common visitor to most parts of the county. The C.B.C. indices, shown below, chart the sudden decline over the winter of 1968/69 which has been linked with the severe drought conditions in the Sahel: the region to the south of the Sahara where the Whitethroats winter. This sudden change was not the result of a single year's drought but came after a series of very dry seasons had caused significant damage to the whole ecology of the wintering area. Most of the Atlas fieldwork was undertaken after this decrease and the map would undoubtedly have been 'blacker' had all the fieldwork been completed in 1967 and 1968. Male Whitethroats, with their cheerful grating song and familiar display-flight, are very conspicuous and they were quite easily found by fieldworkers. Almost any small areas of scrub, even in such unlikely sites as railway yards and allotments surrounded by urban development, may be used by a pair to nest and the typical nest site in such circumstances would be in a nettle-bed — a country name for the species is 'Nettle-creeper'.

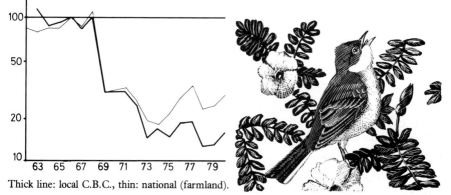

Thick line: local C.B.C., thin: national (farmland).

85

GARDEN WARBLER *Sylvia borin*

Hertfordshire records from
283 tetrads   56%
Bedfordshire   43%
London   43%
Kent   42%
Britain & Ireland   49%
France (Brittany) 83(95)%
Netherlands   91%

Hertfordshire status:
Breeding proved in 56
tetrads (20%) and probable
in 162 more (57%).

A fairly widespread
summer visitor to areas of
wood and scrub. Fre-
quently recorded on
passage.

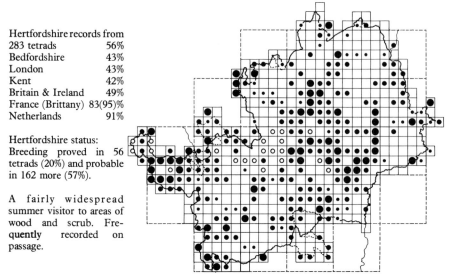

This nondescript species, a medium-sized olive-brown warbler, is a fairly common summer visitor to most of the woods in Hertfordshire. It is nowhere particularly common but may be quite numerous in some rather mature scrubland areas — also favoured by the other *Sylvia* warblers. In some areas substantial numbers nest in newly planted forestry areas *provided* that some small areas of mature trees have been left standing. Many Atlas records came from fieldworkers hearing it sing — unfortunately very similar to the Blackcap and so they were urged to find the singing bird to confirm identity. In general Blackcap's call and song are rather louder than Garden Warbler's. This is a species which has shown a steady and disturbing decline in C.B.C. index on the local plots although, nationally, it would seem to have been relatively stable in the 1960's. Since it winters in the same general area as the Whitethroat this decline may be due to the deterioration of the ecosystem in the Sahel.

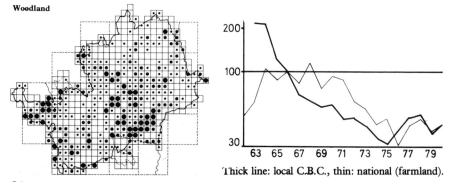

Thick line: local C.B.C., thin: national (farmland).

BLACKCAP   *Sylvia atricapilla*

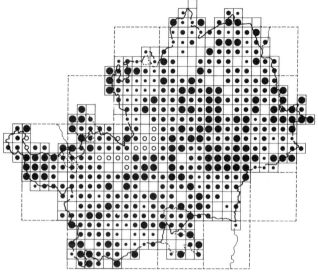

Hertfordshire records from
446 tetrads   88%
Bedfordshire   69%
London   71%
Kent   56%
Britain & Ireland   57%
France (Brittany) 96(95)%
Netherlands   83%

Hertfordshire status:
Breeding proved in 137
tetrads (31%) and probable
in 237 more (53%).

A common summer visitor
to scrub, woodland and
mature gardens. Frequent
on passage: some winter
visitors.

A widespread summer visitor to most areas offering adequate cover the Blackcap is considered by many to rival the Nightingale as a songster. Many of the Atlas records result from this song but, as it is sometimes very like that of the Garden Warbler, the fieldworkers were urged to check the identity of each singing bird by sight. In most areas semi-natural woodland or scrub areas are the main places for breeding birds but damp areas of cover by gravel diggings, thick hedges in farmland, 'mature' gardens in suburbia and even the scrappy scrub of derelict industrial land may also have successful breeding pairs. The Blackcap is a shorter distance migrant than most summer visitors and ringing records suggest that many winter in southern Europe and North Africa. Both the local and national C.B.C. indices show a fairly steady population from the mid 1960's. The low level in 1962, on the national index, is unlikely to be related to the cold winter — the few wintering birds in Britain are probably of central European origin.

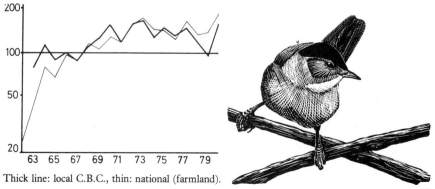

Thick line: local C.B.C., thin: national (farmland).

87

WOOD WARBLER   *Phylloscopus sibilatrix*

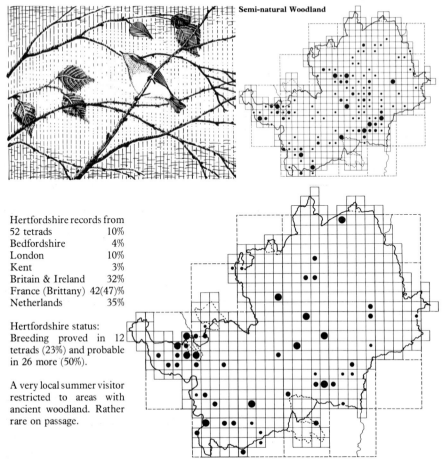

Semi-natural Woodland

Hertfordshire records from
52 tetrads   10%
Bedfordshire   4%
London   10%
Kent   3%
Britain & Ireland   32%
France (Brittany)   42(47)%
Netherlands   35%

Hertfordshire status:
Breeding proved in 12
tetrads (23%) and probable
in 26 more (50%).

A very local summer visitor
restricted to areas with
ancient woodland. Rather
rare on passage.

The relationship between the Atlas distribution and the distribution of semi-
natural woodlands (top right) is clear. The map below was produced by Trevor
James for the two years 1978-79. Although coverage was not complete birds were
found in several new tetrads.

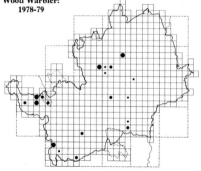

Wood Warbler:
1978-79

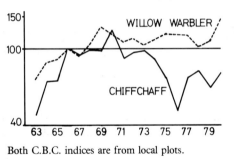

Both C.B.C. indices are from local plots.

CHIFFCHAFF

Phylloscopus collybita

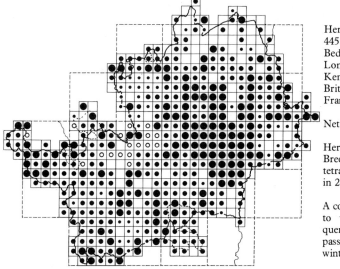

Hertfordshire records from
445 tetrads	88%
Bedfordshire	68%
London	72%
Kent	58%
Britain & Ireland	75%
France (Brittany)	91(100)%
Netherlands	90%

Hertfordshire status:
Breeding proved in 143 tetrads (32%) and probable in 240 more (54%).

A common summer visitor to woodland. Very frequently recorded on spring passage. May sometimes winter.

This very widespread summer visitor was at a high population level locally during the Atlas period (see opposite). The map may include some records of singing birds which were actually migrants that moved onwards later.

WILLOW WARBLER

Phylloscopus trochilus

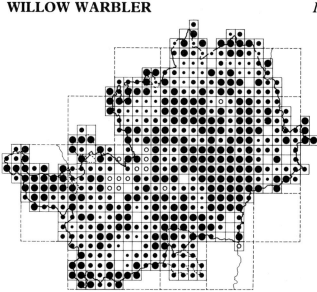

Hertfordshire records from
477 tetrads	95%
Bedfordshire	82%
London	76%
Kent	64%
Britain & Ireland	92%
France (Brittany)	66(93)%
Netherlands	97%

Hertfordshire status:
Breeding proved in 232 tetrads (49%) and probable in 190 more (40%).

An abundant summer visitor to scrub, wood and hedge. Very common on autumn passage from July to mid-September.

Undoubtedly the most numerous warbler in Hertfordshire there are many areas where literally dozens of singing birds are within earshot. Population levels locally seem to have been at a good level since 1966.

GOLDCREST

Regulus regulus

Hertfordshire records from
258 tetrads   51%
Bedfordshire   39%
London   45%
Kent   42%
Britain & Ireland   84%
France (Brittany) 56(85)%
Netherlands   45%

Hertfordshire status:
Breeding proved in 81
tetrads (31%) and probable
in 114 more (44%).

Resident bird particularly
of coniferous woodland.
Much movement outside
the summer. Vulnerable to
harsh winter weather.

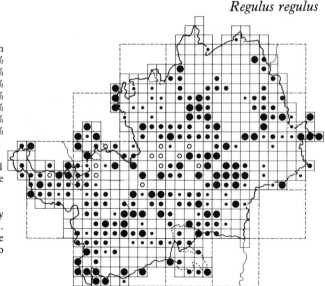

Woodland

Goldcrest populations over the whole of Britain were at a very high level during and for a few years after the Atlas period. In Hertfordshire they could be found breeding in large numbers in many of the newly maturing conifer woods and odd pairs bred in isolated conifers and even deciduous woods. Fieldworkers were often able to find them in churchyard Yews.

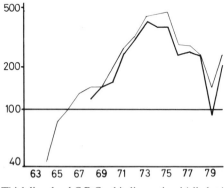

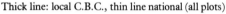

Thick line: local C.B.C., thin line national (all plots)

FIRECREST

Regulus ignicapillus

Two Atlas records of singing birds: TQ09 C and TL00 K were in the west of the county close to the established breeding birds at Wendover (Bucks).

90

SPOTTED FLYCATCHER   *Muscicapa striata*

Hertfordshire records from	
407 tetrads	81%
Bedfordshire	67%
London	69%
Kent	50%
Britain & Ireland	93%
France (Brittany)	68(86)%
Netherlands	84%

Hertfordshire status:
Breeding proved in 213 tetrads (52%) and probable in 88 more (22%).

A common summer visitor to gardens, orchards and woods. Not common on passage.

Thick line: local C.B.C., thin: national (farmland).

The Spotted Flycatcher is a very long-distance migrant reaching the south of Africa. It is the latest migrant to return to breed and may have been missed in a few tetrads which were mainly visited early in the season. Its two requirements in the breeding season are a hole or crevice in which to nest and suitable perches from which to make its feeding flights. Both the national and local (based in rather small samples) C.B.C. indices have been falling since the Census started.

BEARDED TIT   *Panurus biarmicus*

Hertfordshire records from one tetrad	0%
Bedfordshire -%	Britain & Ireland	1%
London	0%	France (Brittany)	3(16)%
Kent	1%	Netherlands	14%

Hertfordshire status:
Breeding proved in one tetrad (100%).

The only successful breeding records were at Stanborough (TL21 F) in 1966 and 1968. Pairs were also present there in 1971, 1972 and 1973. Wintering birds, presumably from the thriving East Anglian population, are regularly recorded particularly at Rye Meads and Tring.

LONG-TAILED TIT

Aegithalos caudatus

Hertfordshire records from
219 tetrads	43%
Bedfordshire	52%
London	46%
Kent	42%
Britain & Ireland	76%
France (Brittany)	89(94)%
Netherlands	61%

Hertfordshire status:
Breeding proved in 115
tetrads (53%) and probable
in 41 more (19%).

A patchily distributed but
locally common bird of
woods and hedges. Flocks
widely during the winter.

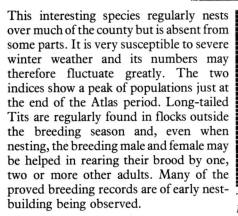

This interesting species regularly nests over much of the county but is absent from some parts. It is very susceptible to severe winter weather and its numbers may therefore fluctuate greatly. The two indices show a peak of populations just at the end of the Atlas period. Long-tailed Tits are regularly found in flocks outside the breeding season and, even when nesting, the breeding male and female may be helped in rearing their brood by one, two or more other adults. Many of the proved breeding records are of early nest-building being observed.

The map below combines the information for Marsh and Willow Tit given opposite. Clearly both species shun the most developed areas and those with intensive arable farming

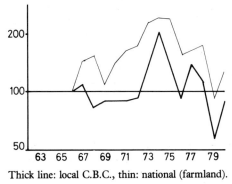

Thick line: local C.B.C., thin: national (farmland).

- ◑ MARSH TIT ONLY
- ◒ WILLOW TIT ONLY
- ● BOTH MARSH & WILLOW

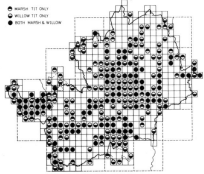

92

MARSH TIT   *Parus palustris*

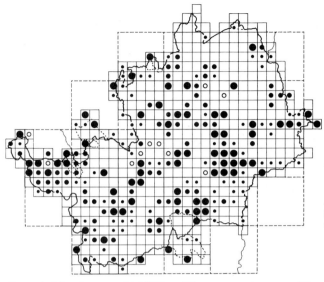

Hertfordshire records from
233 tetrads   46%
Bedfordshire   33%
London   32%
Kent   23%
Britain & Ireland   35%
France (Brittany) 71(83)%
Netherlands   38%

Hertfordshire status:
Breeding proved in 70
tetrads (30%) and probable
in 72 more (31%).

A local resident breeding
species generally of the
more wooded areas.

See combined map with Willow Tit on opposite page. The national C.B.C. index
for this species has dropped quite steadily over the last 15 years by about 30%
overall: in the same period the local index (very small sample) has dropped 60%.

WILLOW TIT   *Parus montanus*

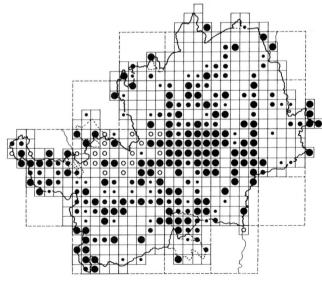

Hertfordshire records from
269 tetrads   53%
Bedfordshire   29%
London   31%
Kent   17%
Britain & Ireland   32%
France (Brittany) 32(-)%
Netherlands   68%

Hertfordshire status:
Breeding proved in 134
tetrads (50%) and probable
in 72 more (27%).

A resident breeding bird of
most wooded areas but
absent from the most open
regions.

See combined map with Marsh Tit on opposite page. No national C.B.C. index is
published but, on local sites, the population has clearly increased two- or three-
fold over the last 15 years.

COAL TIT

Parus ater

Hertfordshire records from
296 tetrads   59%
Bedfordshire   37%
London   63%
Kent   42%
Britain & Ireland 84%
France (Brittany) 47(61)%
Netherlands   42%

Hertfordshire status:
Breeding proved in 141 tetrads (48%) and probable in 89 more (30%).

A fairly common bird in all areas with conifers. Much more local elsewhere save during the winter.

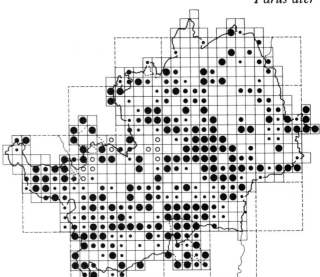

Woodland

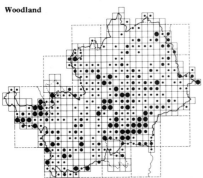

The Coal Tit is the smallest of the three most common tits breeding in Hertfordshire. It is particularly associated with conifers and has a very thin, fine bill adapted for feeding amongst the needles. The local C.B.C. follows the national figures closely. Compared with the other two species it has fluctuated more widely and is both more vulnerable to cold winters (note the decline after 1978/79) and also best able to exploit the areas of maturing conifer plantations.

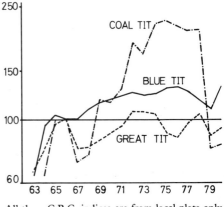

All three C.B.C. indices are from local plots only.

94

BLUE TIT

Parus caeruleus

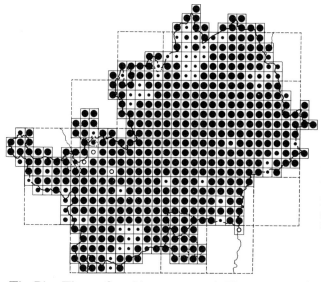

Hertfordshire records from
504 tetrads   100%
Bedfordshire   95%
London   93%
Kent   86%
Britain & Ireland   90%
France (Brittany) 96(95)%
Netherlands   92%

Hertfordshire status:
Breeding proved in 431
tetrads (86%) and probable
in 31 more (6%).

Present everywhere and
abundant in most wood-
land.

The Blue Tit was found in every tetrad. The recovery after the cold winters was rapid and the population has remained relatively stable since then. The local index is in step with the national one for both Blue and Great Tits.

GREAT TIT

Parus major

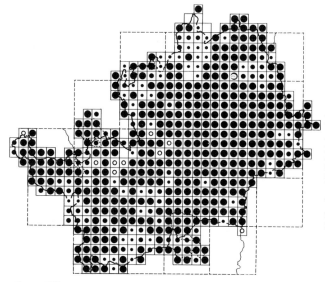

Hertfordshire records from
499 tetrads   99%
Bedfordshire   85%
London   90%
Kent   81%
Britain & Ireland   87%
France (Brittany) 98(98)%
Netherlands   95%

Hertfordshire status:
Breeding proved in 381
tetrads (76%) and probable
in 57 more (11%).

Very common throughout
the year: particularly in the
Beech and Oak woods.

Great Tits are very common in Hertfordshire in woods and gardens and also along mature hedgerows in farmland. Although the C.B.C. shows some effect of the 1962/63 cold weather they generally survive cold winters well.

NUTHATCH

Sitta europaea

Hertfordshire records from
195 tetrads   39%
Bedfordshire   18%
London   47%
Kent   21%
Britain & Ireland   30%
France (Brittany) 81(89)%
Netherlands   32%

Hertfordshire status:
Breeding proved in 80
tetrads (41%) and probable
in 56 more (29%).

Resident in areas of mature
deciduous trees: generally
semi-natural woodland but
also mature gardens.

Semi-natural Woodland

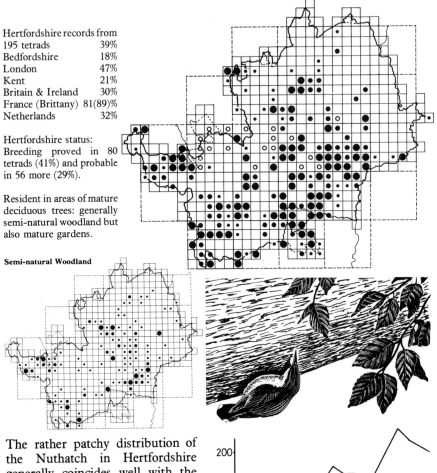

The rather patchy distribution of
the Nuthatch in Hertfordshire
generally coincides well with the
remaining areas of semi-natural
woodland. However, on the
northeastern edge, there is an area
with some extensive woods and no
Nuthatches. On the National Atlas
this is the edge of a blank area
running through Essex and into
Cambridgeshire.

Thick line: local C.B.C., thin: national (woodland)

GOLDEN ORIOLE

Oriolus oriolus

Two Atlas records, both 'column 1', came from TL10 and TL21. The last
published breeding record was in 1881, however there are summer records every
few years and this elusive species may have bred occasionally.

96

TREECREEPER

Certhia familiaris

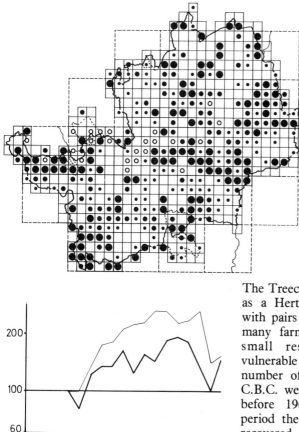

Hertfordshire records from	
320 tetrads	63%
Bedfordshire	46%
London	51%
Kent	32%
Britain & Ireland	78%
France (Brittany)	15(-)%
Netherlands	0%

Hertfordshire status:
Breeding proved in 115 tetrads (36%) and probable in 87 more (27%).

Widespread resident of woodland and locally in some hedges and gardens.

200

100

60

63 65 67 69 71 73 75 77 79

Thick line: local C.B.C., thin: national (farmland).

The Treecreeper is well distributed as a Hertfordshire breeding bird with pairs even in small copses in many farmland areas. As a very small resident species it is vulnerable to cold winters but the number of pairs included in the C.B.C. were too few for an index before 1966. During the Atlas period the population had largely recovered. The national index has consistently run at a higher level than the local one.

RED-BACKED SHRIKE

Lanius collurio

Hertfordshire records from 15 tetrads		3%
Bedfordshire	2%	Britain & Ireland	3%
London	1%	France (Brittany)	60(15)%
Kent	0%	Netherlands	10%

Hertfordshire status:
Breeding proved in eight tetrads (53%) and probable in one more (7%).

Formerly a widespread and common breeding species but nesting in Hertfordshire is now very irregular. Apart from a pair nesting at a traditional site near Hertford and another in TL43 the proved and probable breeding records came from the Chiltern scarp.

97

JAY

Garrulus glandarius

Hertfordshire records from
351 tetrads   70%
Bedfordshire   40%
London   74%
Kent   51%
Britain & Ireland   55%
France (Brittany) 95(92)%
Netherlands   73%

Hertfordshire status:
Breeding proved in 122
tetrads (35%) and probable
in 76 more (22%).

A fairly widespread nesting
species confined to wood-
land and mature gardens.
Some local movements in
the autumn.

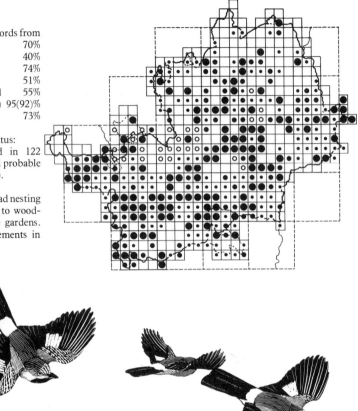

The Jay is the crow of woodland areas and the Atlas map agrees closely with the
distribution of woodland within the county. The C.B.C. index (local plots only)
indicates that the Jay population is fairly stable.

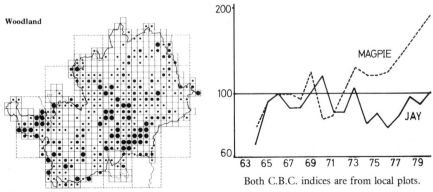

Both C.B.C. indices are from local plots.

MAGPIE

Pica pica

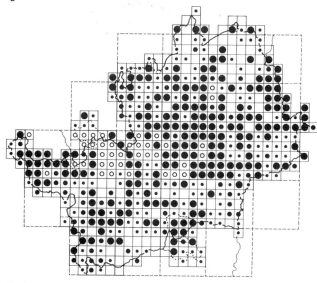

Hertfordshire records from

376 tetrads	75%
Bedfordshire	51%
London	77%
Kent	65%
Britain & Ireland	75%
France (Brittany)	93(99)%
Netherlands	90%

Hertfordshire status:
Breeding proved in 212 tetrads (56%) and probable in 42 more (11%).

A resident bird of farm hedges, copses and woodland edge. Increasingly found in suburban areas.

Since their nests are so very conspicuous Magpies are amongst the easiest species to prove breeding. Their populations fluctuated locally during the Atlas period but, over the last few years, have increased sharply in line with the national trend.

JACKDAW

Corvus monedula

Hertfordshire records from

433 tetrads	86%
Bedfordshire	72%
London	54%
Kent	62%
Britain & Ireland	88%
France (Brittany)	74(88)%
Netherlands	87%

Hertfordshire status:
Breeding proved in 204 tetrads (47%) and probable in 54 more (12%).

Widespread and resident semi-colonial species. Nests in holes in mature trees or buildings (often chimneys).

Jackdaws are very noisy and conspicuous birds easy to locate during the breeding season. The national population index has remained fairly static over the last 15 years but the local one, based on rather small samples, has shown a fluctuating but quite steady increase over the same period.

ROOK

Corvus frugilegus

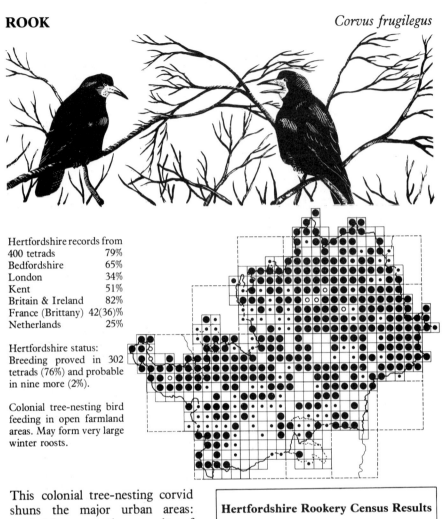

Hertfordshire records from
400 tetrads   79%
Bedfordshire   65%
London   34%
Kent   51%
Britain & Ireland   82%
France (Brittany) 42(36)%
Netherlands   25%

Hertfordshire status:
Breeding proved in 302
tetrads (76%) and probable
in nine more (2%).

Colonial tree-nesting bird
feeding in open farmland
areas. May form very large
winter roosts.

This colonial tree-nesting corvid shuns the major urban areas: probably not the result of disturbance whilst breeding but because most towns do not have suitable open areas for feeding. A series of counts of Hertfordshire rookeries have been organised over the period 1945-1975, largely by Bryan Sage. The

Hertfordshire Rookery Census Results		
Year	*Nests*	*% change*
1945	8519	
1960/61	15739	+ 84.8
1971	10632	– 32.5
1975	8700	– 18.2

results, shown in the table, indicate that a recent and rapid decline, which is also shown by the national figures, has set in. During the two most recent surveys about 400 rookeries were found: about 25% down on the 1960/61 figures. The decline may be related both to the spread of Dutch Elm disease and the loss of nesting trees and also to the loss of the Rook's most important feeding habitat — permanent pasture.

100

CROW
Corvus corone

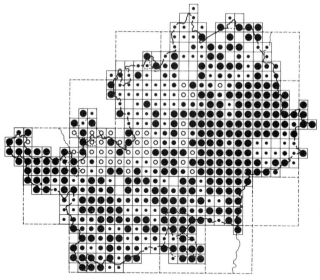

Hertfordshire records from
480 tetrads	95%
Bedfordshire	82%
London	90%
Kent	68%
Britain & Ireland	98%
France (Brittany)	
	96(100)%
Netherlands	90%

Hertfordshire status:
Breeding proved in 266 tetrads (55%) and probable in 70 more (15%).

Very common territorial and solitary nesting bird found in all areas, including town centres.

The Carrion Crow is present throughout the county despite the best efforts of the gamekeepers. The C.B.C. indices (see below) show a fairly steady increase in population both nationally and locally. A similar index of gamekeeping activity would almost certainly show a continuing steady decline. The two are linked for the Carrion Crow is the number one enemy of the keeper where gamebirds or ducks are rearing their broods in the wild. As these pressures have been eased so the amount of road traffic and its speed have increased. Inevitably this has led to an increasing supply of bodies of small birds and mammals to be scavenged. Any sort of countryside is suitable for a territory provided that a single tree, bush or even electricity pylon is available for nesting. In urban areas the birds may breed on buildings or in trees in parks or gardens. These pairs often feed in the open areas of town parks during the day but may come down to road casualties in urban streets during the early morning when they are unlikely to be disturbed.

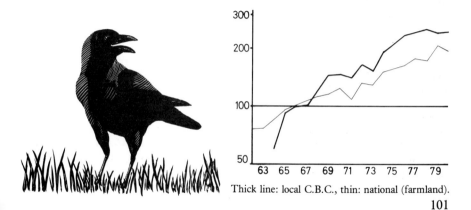

Thick line: local C.B.C., thin: national (farmland).

101

STARLING

Sturnus vulgaris

Hertfordshire records from
504 tetrads   100%
Bedfordshire   100%
London   96%
Kent   92%
Britain & Ireland 96%
France (Brittany)
                          90(100)%
Netherlands   96%

Hertfordshire status:
Breeding proved in 469
tetrads (93%) and probable
in nine more (2%).

Abundant resident species
nesting in holes in trees or
buildings. Vast numbers of
immigrants arrive in winter
when huge roosts form.

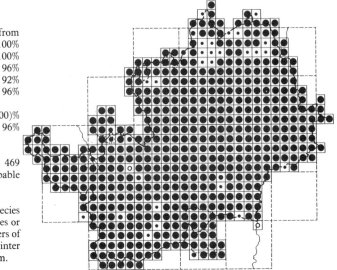

HOUSE SPARROW

Passer domesticus

Hertfordshire records from
502 tetrads   100%
Bedfordshire   100%
London   96%
Kent   94%
Britain & Ireland 94%
France (Brittany)
                          99(100)%
Netherlands   96%

Hertfordshire status:
Breeding proved in 466
tetrads (93%) and probable
in nine more (2%).

Abundant resident bird.
Everywhere associated
with man: generally breeds
on or in buildings.

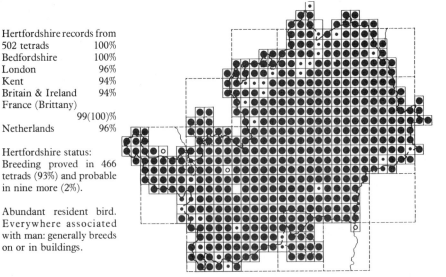

Although still very widespread and common it is probable that the House Sparrow
has declined over the last 70 years. When the horse provided the usual means of
transport there must have been many extra opportunities for this adaptable species
to gather food. The loss of this source of supply may have been offset, to some
extent, by the enormous amount of food which they now take from birdtables.

TREE SPARROW

Passer montanus

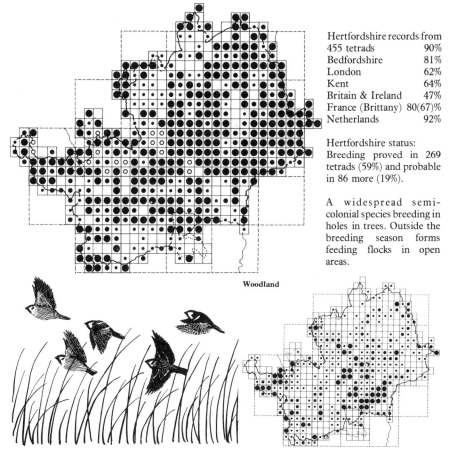

Hertfordshire records from
455 tetrads	90%
Bedfordshire	81%
London	62%
Kent	64%
Britain & Ireland	47%
France (Brittany)	80(67)%
Netherlands	92%

Hertfordshire status:
Breeding proved in 269 tetrads (59%) and probable in 86 more (19%).

A widespread semi-colonial species breeding in holes in trees. Outside the breeding season forms feeding flocks in open areas.

Woodland

The Tree Sparrow is a common bird of most rural areas in Hertfordshire. Early in the breeding season they may readily be located for the males persistently 'chip', the species' most characteristic call, from the vicinity of the nest. This becomes much less obvious as the season progresses and successive nesting attempts become out of phase. There are few areas of wood without their breeding birds and some substantial colonies have built up, particularly in nest-box schemes. Such concentrations may be short-lived as the local populations shift. Over the last two years both the local and national C.B.C. indices have suddenly dropped sharply and there is no doubt that Tree Sparrows are now much rarer than they were.

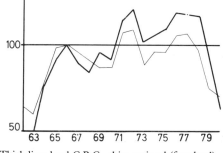

Thick line: local C.B.C., thin: national (farmland).

103

CHAFFINCH

Fringilla coelebs

Hertfordshire records from
499 tetrads	99%
Bedfordshire	93%
London	90%
Kent	82%
Britain & Ireland	92%
France (Brittany)	98(95)%
Netherlands	88%

Hertfordshire status:
Breeding proved in 291 tetrads (58%) and probable in 140 more (28%).

A very common resident of woods, gardens and hedges (with trees for song-posts). Augmented by many visitors in winter flocks.

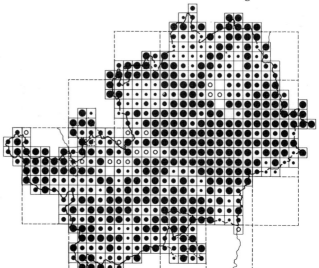

Both the local and national Chaffinch C.B.C. indices were at a slightly lower level during most of the Atlas period than immediately before or after. However, with such a common species, this is not likely to have affected the map.

GREENFINCH

Carduelis chloris

Hertfordshire records from
491 tetrads	97%
Bedfordshire	96%
London	94%
Kent	85%
Britain & Ireland	86%
France (Brittany)	93(100)%
Netherlands	91%

Hertfordshire status:
Breeding proved in 261 tetrads (53%) and probable in 177 more (36%).

Widespread, partly colonial, nesting species of scrub and garden. Mobile outside breeding season and often forms flocks.

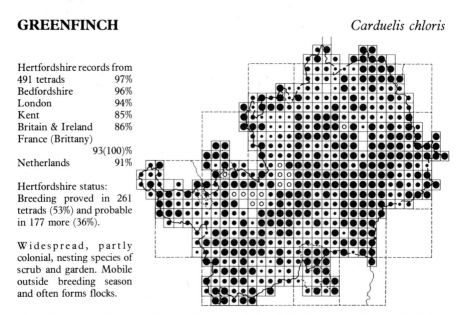

The slight trough shown by the Greenfinch local C.B.C. index during the Atlas period is not apparent in the national index which, on farmland, was between 98 and 101 for the whole period.

GOLDFINCH

Carduelis carduelis

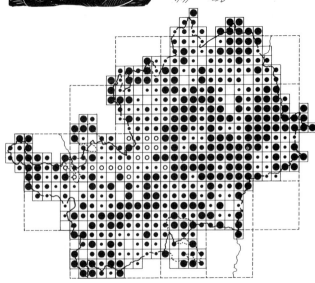

Hertfordshire records from
472 tetrads 94%
Bedfordshire 88%
London 86%
Kent 77%
Britain & Ireland 78%
France (Brittany) 96(99)%
Netherlands 44%

Hertfordshire status:
Breeding proved in 227
tetrads (48%) and probable
in 148 more (31%).

A common breeding bird
often in orchards or
gardens. Flocks formed in
the autumn but many leave
the country for the winter.

This attractive finch is widely but patchly distributed throughout the county in rural, suburban and even urban areas. The local C.B.C. index shows a serious fall in 1969 not seen in the national figures: these doubled between 1966 and 1977. It therefore seems that Hertfordshire Goldfinch populations are not keeping pace with the rest of the country. Possibly the increased use of weedkillers with the intensification of agriculture and even the mechanical cutting of roadside verges may be implicated.

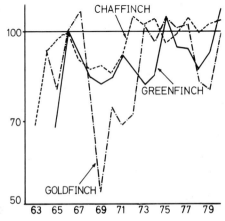

All three C.B.C. indices are from local plots only.

105

SISKIN

Carduelis spinus

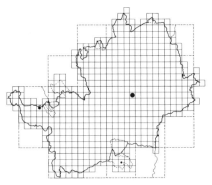

Hertfordshire records from three tetrads			1%
Bedfordshire	1%	Britain & Ireland	22%
London	1%	France (Brittany)	6(-)%
Kent	1%	Netherlands	10%

Hertfordshire status:
Breeding proved in one tetrad (33%) and probable in one more (33%).

The only breeding records have been in Bramfield Forest (TL21 Y) and suspected in Ashridge (SP91 R). There was also a 'column 1' record from TQ29. This attractive little finch is a regular winter visitor found particularly on Alder and, in some years, on seeding Birch.

LINNET

Carduelis cannabina

Hertfordshire records from
482 tetrads	96%
Bedfordshire	93%
London	80%
Kent	82%
Britain & Ireland	87%
France (Brittany)	
	88(100)%
Netherlands	96%

Hertfordshire status:
Breeding proved in 232 tetrads (48%) and probable in 156 more (32%).

A common breeding bird of scrub, hedge and garden. Flocks, sometimes large, are formed outside the breeding season.

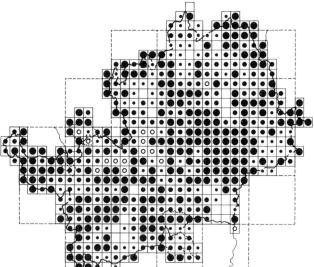

Although Linnets breed over most of the county there are a few built-up areas without any. Some farmland regions have substantial populations but the major colonies are generally in Hawthorn scrub. Both nationally and locally the C.B.C. index has fluctuated over the last 12 years but the figures show a cold weather effect in the early 1960's.

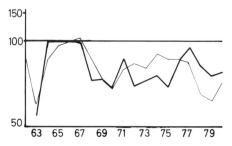

Thick line: local C.B.C., thin: national (farmland).

106

REDPOLL   *Carduelis flammea*

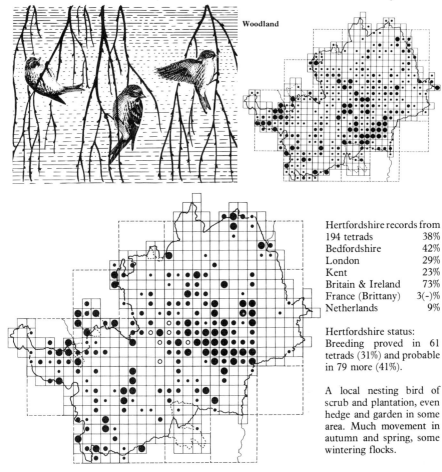

Woodland

Hertfordshire records from
194 tetrads	38%
Bedfordshire	42%
London	29%
Kent	23%
Britain & Ireland	73%
France (Brittany)	3(-)%
Netherlands	9%

Hertfordshire status:
Breeding proved in 61
tetrads (31%) and probable
in 79 more (41%).

A local nesting bird of
scrub and plantation, even
hedge and garden in some
area. Much movement in
autumn and spring, some
wintering flocks.

The map shows that Redpolls are
fairly common in the more wooded
areas of Hertfordshire. The
National Atlas map shows that we
are on the eastern edge of a huge gap
in Redpoll breeding distribution
extending from south Wales to
Buckinghamshire. However the
C.B.C. indices show that the species
was increasing rapidly during the
1960's and beyond. Birds were
found breeding in gardens and along
farm hedges during the Atlas
fieldwork and not just in woodland
edges and scrubby areas.

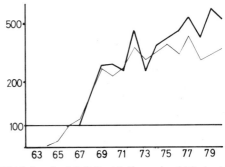

Thick line: local C.B.C., thin line national (all plots)

107

COMMON CROSSBILL

Loxia curvirostra

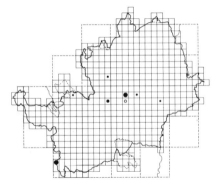

Hertfordshire records from eight tetrads		2%
Bedfordshire	2%	Britain & Ireland	8%
London	0%	France (Brittany)	13(-)%
Kent	1%	Netherlands	6%

Hertfordshire status:
Breeding proved in two tetrads (25%) and probable in one more (13%).

Bred regularly in Bramfield Forest area (TL21) from 1944 to 1975. Otherwise irregular breeding records have followed irruptions. If conifer plantations are allowed to stand and mature their cone crops may encourage more regular breeding of this specialist species.

BULLFINCH

Pyrrhula pyrrhula

Hertfordshire records from	
475 tetrads	94%
Bedfordshire	86%
London	77%
Kent	70%
Britain & Ireland	83%
France (Brittany)	80(98)%
Netherlands	43%

Hertfordshire status:
Breeding proved in 252 tetrads (53%) and probable in 127 more (27%).

A very common species of hedge, wood and garden. Only absent from areas which lack suitable cover.

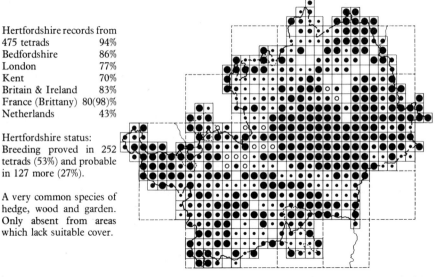

Breeding Bullfinches prefer thick hedges, scrub or woodland and are probably genuinely absent from parts of the northeast of the county. The C.B.C. graphs show that the local and national indices have kept fairly well in step until 1980 when the local population increased.

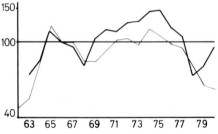

Thick line: local C.B.C., thin: national (farmland).

HAWFINCH

Coccothraustes coccothraustes

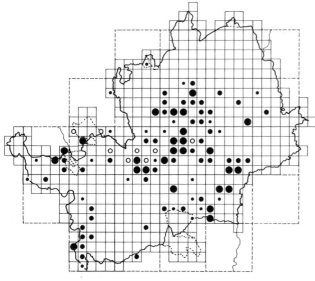

Hertfordshire records from
109 tetrads	22%
Bedfordshire	8%
London	9%
Kent	8%
Britain & Ireland	12%
France (Brittany)	39(30)%
Netherlands	20%

Hertfordshire status:
Breeding proved in 33 tetrads (30%) & probable in 47 more (43%).

Local resident breeding bird, mainly in areas with some remnants of ancient woodlands.

One of the surprises of the Atlas fieldwork was the number of tetrad records we received for this elusive species. Clearly Hertfordshire is one of the national strongholds of the Hawfinch and they are mostly found in or near the major areas of woodland shown in the map below. Most birdwatchers seldom record this species unless they are used to hearing the characteristic 'tzik' flight call. The proved breeding records came both from nests being found, generally high in a tree among thin branches and often visible from the ground, or from lucky observations of family parties, usually at drinking pools. The bird's large and, to the birdringer, fearsome bill is adapted for cracking open hard food items, like cherry stones, to extract the kernel. In many places the birds are associated with food-bearing trees – wild cherries, hornbeam, beech and sycamore in the woods and cherries in orchards. On the Ashridge estate, in SP 91, a loose colony of eight or nine pairs were discovered in a few hundred square metres of birch but, probably, the majority of tetrad records involve many fewer birds. Local movements from the breeding area during the winter may take place.

Semi-natural Woodland

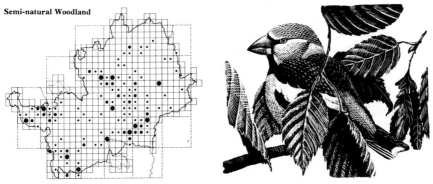

YELLOWHAMMER

Emberiza citrinella

Hertfordshire records from
475 tetrads	94%
Bedfordshire	96%
London	59%
Kent	72%
Britain & Ireland	88%
France (Brittany)	81(99)%
Netherlands	56%

Hertfordshire status:
Breeding proved in 224
tetrads (47%) and probable
in 206 more (43%).

A common resident species
of scrub and open farm-
land. Probably mobile only
during hard weather: large
flocks may form in winter.

Yellowhammers are absent from many of the more developed areas of the southern
part of the county. Although there may be suitable nest sites and feeding areas
available they seem to be vulnerable to disturbance. In farmland areas it must have
some songposts within its territory but these may be fairly low — a row of
fenceposts will do just as well as a row of telegraph poles. The nest is generally set
in a hedge bottom and concealed in a
tussock of grass. In areas where
hedges are maintained mechanically
and cut very low the Yellowhammer
is one of the few birds not to be badly
affected — unless its song posts are
also cut down. The local C.B.C.
seems to have run ahead of the
national level until 1978.

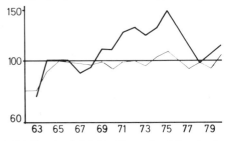

Thick line: local C.B.C., thin: national (farmland).

110

CIRL BUNTING *Emberiza cirlus*

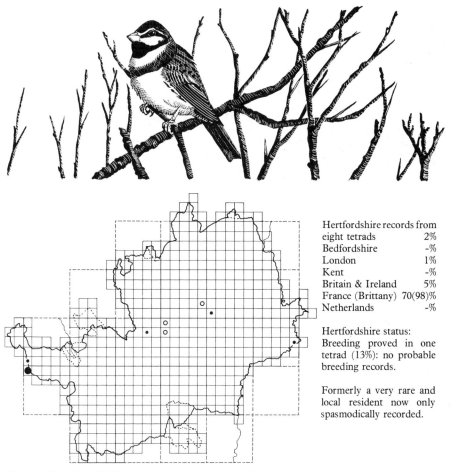

Hertfordshire records from
eight tetrads   2%
Bedfordshire   -%
London   1%
Kent   -%
Britain & Ireland   5%
France (Brittany)   70(98)%
Netherlands   -%

Hertfordshire status:
Breeding proved in one
tetrad (13%): no probable
breeding records.

Formerly a very rare and
local resident now only
spasmodically recorded.

At one time the Cirl Bunting was a local speciality along the northwestern edge of the Chilterns. In the vicinity of Tring these birds could regularly be found in Hertfordshire. Breeding was proved here during the Atlas period but there have been no records from this area for several years. The other Atlas records reflected the species' previous status as 'a very local resident' but it must now be considered extinct in the county: the only record since the completion of the Atlas was in TQ09 during June 1977. In Britain as a whole, the Cirl Bunting has contracted its range and become very much rarer over the last 50 years. It is difficult to understand this decline for there were records at the beginning of the century of it being far commoner than the Yellowhammer in some parts of Kent on chalk downland. Possibly the reduction in sheep-grazing and the loss of so many rabbits to myxomatosis has allowed the grass to grow so much that the Cirl Bunting has been excluded where the Yellowhammer is still able to forage. In their remaining British stronghold, Devon, they are also less likely to suffer from really severe winter weather.

111

REED BUNTING

Emberiza schoeniclus

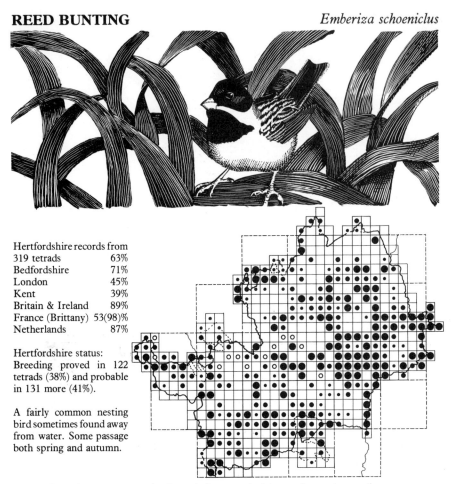

Hertfordshire records from
319 tetrads   63%
Bedfordshire   71%
London   45%
Kent   39%
Britain & Ireland   89%
France (Brittany) 53(98)%
Netherlands   87%

Hertfordshire status:
Breeding proved in 122
tetrads (38%) and probable
in 131 more (41%).

A fairly common nesting
bird sometimes found away
from water. Some passage
both spring and autumn.

Reed Buntings commonly breed in wet habitats throughout the county —
provided there are dense tangles of rank vegetation or reed-beds. In some areas
they also breed in corn crops and dry grassland — even high on the chalk. The
species is badly hit by very cold winters.

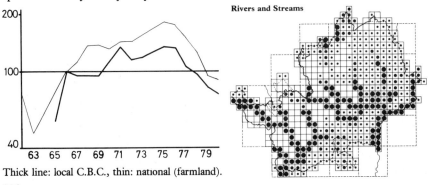

Thick line: local C.B.C., thin: national (farmland).

CORN BUNTING

Miliaria calandra

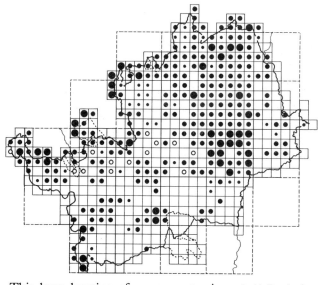

Hertfordshire records from
302 tetrads   60%
Bedfordshire   60%
London   17%
Kent   28%
Britain & Ireland   37%
France (Brittany) 74(51)%
Netherlands   18%

Hertfordshire status:
Breeding proved in 40
tetrads (13%) and probable
in 209 more (69%).

A resident breeding bird
over most of the north but
very local in the south of
the county.

This large bunting of open country is a very easy species to survey as territorial males sing from prominent song posts. In Hertfordshire it is locally common but inexplicably absent in other parts. A patchy distribution is very much what was expected and it reflects, at the local level, what was discovered from the National Atlas. The main correlate is the presence of arable farmland (and possibly the absence of grass). The local C.B.C. indicates an increase whilst the population nationally has declined: possibly this is a bird which benefits from the modern agricultural techniques.

Arable Farmland

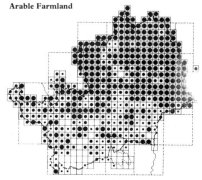

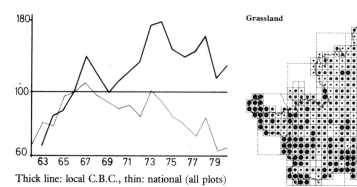

Thick line: local C.B.C., thin: national (all plots)

Grassland

113

All species recorded in the county and not wholly dismissed as escapes from captivity are included. Those for which records are required by the County Bird Recorder are marked as follows:

  *   Breeding records and records of flocks needed
  †   All records needed but description not generally necessary
  ‡   All records needed, records will be considered by the County Records Committee
  **   All records needed, records will be considered by the *British Birds* Rarities Committee

The summaries of records by years count multiple sightings of the same individual and also sightings of flocks as single records. The moderately rare species with entries like ':70,74,75(2),79.' give a complete summary of the records for the decade 1970-1979. In this case single records in 1970, 1974 and 1979 and with two in 1975. The page references given refer to the Atlas entries. Species whose records appear in italics have not been recorded in the wild for the last fifty years. These records are summarised from Sage (1959), Sage (1980) and the County Bird Reports up to 1979 which have been published by the Hertfordshire Natural History Society.

‡   Red-throated Diver *Gavia stellata.* Rare, mostly in winter: 72(2),75,79(2).
‡   Black-throated Diver *Gavia arctica.* Rare, mostly in winter: 76,79(3).
‡   Great Northern Diver *Gavia immer.* Rare, mostly in winter: 72,74,77,78.
   Little Grebe *Tachybaptus ruficollis.* Common: see page 22.
*   Great Crested Grebe *Podiceps cristatus.* Resident and winter visitor: see page 23.
‡   Red-necked Grebe *Podiceps grisegena.* Irregular winter visitor: 70(2),71,78(2),79(15).
‡   Slavonian Grebe *Podiceps auritus.* Rare in winter and on passage: 1–3 most years.
‡   Black-necked Grebe *Podiceps nigricollis.* Bred in 1918-1928 but now rare in winter and on passage: 1-4 most years.
‡   Fulmar *Fulmarus glacialis.* Only three records 1956,1959 and 1974.
‡   Manx Shearwater *Puffinus puffinus.* Rare vagrant, usually autumn: 74,77,78.
‡   Storm Petrel *Hydrobates pelagicus.* Five records: 1876,1881,1886,1907,1963.
‡   Leach's Petrel *Oceanodroma leucorhoa.* Autumn storm-driven vagrant: 77(2),78.
‡   Gannet *Sula bassana.* Rare vagrant: 70,71,74,76.
†   Cormorant *Phalacrocorax carbo.* Regularly recorded at all seasons.
†   Shag *Phalacrocorax aristotelis.* Irregular vagrant, sometimes numerous.
†   Bittern *Botaurus stellaris.* Bred 1849: now recorded annually, mostly winter.
**   Little Bittern *Ixobrychus minutus.* Rare vagrant: seventh in 1979.
**   Night Heron *Nycticorax nycticorax.* Four records only: 1970,1971 and 1972(2).
**   Squacco Heron *Ardeola ralloides.* Only one record: 1979.
*   Grey Heron *Ardea cinerea.* Local birds supplemented in winter: see page 24.
**   Purple Heron *Ardea purpurea.* Rare vagrant: seventh record in 1978.
**   White Stork *Ciconia ciconia.* Only recorded twice: 1960 and 1978.
**   Glossy Ibis *Plegadis falcinellus. Three records: 1826,1881 and 1887.*
‡   Spoonbill *Platalea leucorodia.* Only two records: 1947 and 1957.
*   Mute Swan *Cygnus olor.* Widespread throughout the year: see page 25.
‡   Bewick's Swan *Cygnus columbianus.* Regular on passage and in winter: 2-8 records *p.a.*
‡   Whooper Swan *Cygnus cygnus.* Rare on passage and during winter: 70(2),72,76.
‡   Bean Goose *Anser fabalis.* The only record was in 1979.

‡   Pink-footed Goose *Anser brachyrhynchus*. Many records may be of escapes: wild flock 1979.

‡   White-fronted Goose *Anser albifrons*. Irregular winter visitor: 70,76(2),77.

*   Greylag Goose *Anser anser*. Resident feral birds: see page 27.

*   Canada Goose *Branta canadensis*. Resident feral birds: see page 26.

‡   Barnacle Goose *Branta leucopsis*. All so far recorded may be escapes.

‡   Brent Goose *Branta bernicla*. Rare winter vagrant: 74,76,77.

†   Egyptian Goose *Alopochen aegyptiacus*. Feral birds recorded since 1974.

†   Shelduck *Tadorna tadorna*. Rare but regular visitor at all seasons.

†   Mandarin *Aix galericulata*. Feral birds spreading into county: see page 27.

†   Wigeon *Anas penelope*. Winter visitor and passage migrant.

** American Wigeon *Anas americana*. First and only record in 1971.

†   Gadwall *Anas strepera*. Regular on passage and in winter: has bred, see page 27.

*   Teal *Anas crecca*. Common in winter and on passage: has bred, see page 28.
    Mallard *Anas platyrhynchos*. Common: see page 29.

†   Pintail *Anas acuta*. Regular winter visitor and passage migrant.

†   Garganey *Anas querquedula*. Regular on passage: has bred twice (1928,1931): see page 29.

** Blue-winged Teal *Anas discors*. One record only: 1978.

*   Shoveler *Anas clypeata*. Common passage and winter, scarce breeder: see page 28.

‡   Red-crested Pochard *Netta rufina*. Regularly recorded — some escapes?
    Pochard *Aythya ferina*. Fairly common throughout year, sparse breeder: see page 30.

** Ring-necked Duck *Aythya collaris*. Three records: 1974,1977(2).

‡   Ferruginous Duck *Aythya nyroca*. Irregularly recorded: 70,71(2),72(2).
    Tufted Duck *Aythya fuligula*. Common: see page 31.

‡   Scaup *Aythya marila*. Regular on passage and in winter: up to 8 records annually.

‡   Eider *Somateria mollissima*. Only five records: 1961,1963,1965(2),1977.

‡   Long-tailed Duck *Clangula hyemalis*. Rare, mostly winter: 72,73,79.

†   Common Scoter *Melanitta nigra*. Scarce, winter and passage: annual.

‡   Velvet Scoter *Melanitta fusca*. Four records: 1930,1963,1976,1979.

†   Goldeneye *Bucephala clangula*. Regular winter visitor.

†   Smew *Mergus albellus*. Irregular winter visitor: almost annual.

‡   Red-breasted Merganser *Mergus serrator*. Irregular winter visitor: almost annual.

†   Goosander *Mergus merganser*. Regular winter visitor.

†   Ruddy Duck *Oxyura jamaicensis*. Feral birds scarce but resident: see page 31.

‡   Honey Buzzard *Pernis apivorus*. Five records in 1800's: one since in 1976.

‡   Red Kite *Milvus milvus*. Only two records this century: 1972,1977.

** White-tailed Eagle *Haliaeetus albicilla*. *Two records in mid-1800's.*

‡   Marsh Harrier *Circus aeruginosus*. Irregular on passage: 1-4 each year since 73.

‡   Hen Harrier *Circus cyaneus*. Irregular winter and passage: 70(2),75(2),78,79(7).

‡   Montagu's Harrier *Circus pygargus*. Has bred (last 1945), now rare passage: 77,78(2),79.

‡   Goshawk *Accipiter gentilis*. The only two records were in 1967 and 1970.

†   Sparrowhawk *Accipiter nisus*. Once more widely distributed: see page 32.

†   Buzzard *Buteo buteo*. Formerly bred, now regularly recorded and may breed again: see page 32.

‡   Rough-legged Buzzard *Buteo lagopus*. Irregular winter visitor: 71,74(2),75(2).

‡   Osprey *Pandion haliaetus*. Almost regular on passage: 71(2),72,73(3),74,76(4),77(3),78(7).

*   Kestrel *Falco tinnunculus*. Common: see page 33.

‡   Merlin *Falco columbarius*. Irregular on passage and in winter: 77,78(2),79(4).

115

‡ Hobby *Falco subbuteo*. Regular summer visitor, sparse: see page 33.
‡ Peregrine *Falco peregrinus*. Irregularly recorded on passage: 76(3),79.
* Red-legged Partridge *Alectoris rufa*. Common: see page 34.
* Grey Partridge *Perdix perdix*. Common: see page 35.
‡ Quail *Coturnix coturnix*. Sparse and irregular summer visitor: see page 36.
  Pheasant *Phasianus colchicus*. Common: see page 37.
‡ Golden Pheasant *Chrysolophus pictus*. Recorded only during 1974,1977 and 1978.
‡ Lady Amherst's Pheasant *Chrysolophus amherstiae*. A handful of recent records: see page 37.
† Water Rail *Rallus aquaticus*. Breeding birds supplemented in winter: see page 38.
‡ Spotted Crake *Porzana porzana*. Rare visitor, has bred once: see page 39.
** Little Crake *Porzana parva*. The only record was in 1953.
** Baillon's Crake *Porzana pusilla*. *The only record was in 1891.*
‡ Corncrake *Crex crex*. Formerly common summer visitor, now very rare on passage: 70,75: see page 39.
  Moorhen *Gallinula chloropus*. Common: see page 40.
  Coot *Fulica atra*. Common: see page 41.
** Great Bustard *Otis tarda*. *Probably bred into 1800's: none recorded since.*
† Oystercatcher *Haematopus ostralegus*. Passage migrant: almost annual (none 71).
‡ Avocet *Recurvirostra avosetta*. All five records recent: 73,74,76(2),78.
† Stone Curlew *Burhinus oedicnemus*. Still breeds in north: see page 43.
† Little Ringed Plover *Charadrius dubius*. Scarce in summer and on passage: see page 42.
† Ringed Plover *Charadrius hiaticula*. Passage migrant, 2 breeding records: see page 43.
‡ Kentish Plover *Charadrius alexandrinus*. Only three records: 1964,1976(2).
‡ Dotterel *Charadrius morinellus*. Rare passage migrant (mostly May): 73(2),79(2).
* Golden Plover *Pluvialis apricaria*. Regular in winter and on passage.
† Grey Plover *Pluvialis squatarola*. Rare in winter and on passage: 74,76(5),77,79.
** Sociable Plover *Chettusia gregaria*. A single record in 1961.
  Lapwing *Vanellus vanellus*. Common, particularly in winter: see page 44.
† Knot *Calidris canutus*. Irregular on passage and in winter: 70,73,75,76,78,79.
† Sanderling *Calidris alba*. Passage migrant: 70,73(8)74,76(5),77,78(2).
† Little Stint *Calidris minuta*. Passage migrant: recorded most years.
‡ Temminck's Stint *Calidris temminckii*. Rare passage migrant: 76,77(2).
‡ Pectoral Sandpiper *Calidris melanotos*. Only five records: 73,77.
† Curlew Sandpiper *Calidris ferruginea*. Irregular on passage: 70(3),73(2),75,76(3),77(2).
‡ Purple Sandpiper *Calidris maritima*. Three records only: 1959,1967 and 1968.
† Dunlin *Calidris alpina*. Regular passage migrant and in winter.
** Broad-billed Sandpiper *Limicola falcinellus*. Only two records: 1946 and 1958.
† Ruff *Philomachus pugnax*. Regular on passage, some winter records.
† Jack Snipe *Lymnocryptes minimus*. Regular winter visitor and passage migrant.
* Snipe *Gallinago gallinago*. Common in winter, sparse breeder: see page 45.
** Great Snipe *Gallinago media*. Very rare vagrant: last recorded 1952.
** Long-billed Dowitcher *Limnodromus scolopaceus*. The single record was in 1977.
† Woodcock *Scolopax rusticola*. Well distributed breeder and winter visitor: see page 46.
† Black-tailed Godwit *Limosa limosa*. Irregular on passage: 71,74(3),75(3),76(6),78.
† Bar-tailed Godwit *Limosa lapponica*. Irregular on passage: 71,73(2),76(5),78,79.
† Whimbrel *Numenius phaeopus*. Regular on passage: usually in flight.
† Curlew *Numenius arquata*. Regularly recorded: not proved to breed: see page 47.
† Spotted Redshank *Tringa erythropus*. Regular passage migrant: almost annual.
† Redshank *Tringa totanus*. Regularly recorded, sparse breeder: see page 48.

** Marsh Sandpiper *Tringa stagnatilis. The only record was in 1887.*
† Greenshank *Tringa nebularia.* Regular passage migrant.
** Lesser Yellowlegs *Tringa flavipes.* The only record was in 1953.
** Solitary Sandpiper *Tringa solitaria.* Only one recorded: 1967.
† Green Sandpiper *Tringa ochropus.* Regular on passage and during winter.
‡ Wood Sandpiper *Tringa glareola.* Passage migrant: almost annual.
† Common Sandpiper *Actitis hypoleucos.* Regular on passage, few have bred: see page 49.
** Spotted Sandpiper *Actitis macularia.* A single record in 1956.
† Turnstone *Arenaria interpres.* Rare on passage: 71,73(4),74(2),75,76(6),78(2).
‡ Red-necked Phalarope *Phalaropus lobatus.* Only four records: 1885,1948,1959 and 1966.
‡ Grey Phalarope *Phalaropus fulicarius.* Very irregular on passage, last in 1960 and 1961.
‡ Pomarine Skua *Stercorarius pomarinus. Only two records: 1914 and 1928.*
‡ Arctic Skua *Stercorarius parasiticus.* Rare vagrant: only 1970's record in 78.
‡ Long-tailed Skua *Stercorarius longicaudus.* The only record was in 1937.
‡ Great Skua *Stercorarius skua.* Only recorded twice: 1867 and 1962.
† Little Gull *Larus minutus.* Regular on passage.
　Black-headed Gull *Larus ridibundus.* Common, even in summer: bred irregularly 1950-64.
　Common Gull *Larus canus.* Commonly recorded in winter and on passage.
　Lesser Black-backed Gull *Larus fuscus.* Passage migrant and winter visitor.
　Herring Gull *Larus argentatus.* Common in winter and on passage.
‡ Iceland Gull *Larus glaucoides.* The only two records were in 1963 and 1965.
‡ Glaucous Gull *Larus hyperboreus.* Rare winter visitor: 76,77,79.
　Great Black-backed Gull *Larus marinus.* Regular in winter and on passage.
† Kittiwake *Rissa tridactyla.* Irregular (storm-driven): 70(2),71,72(2),78(2),79(3).
† Sandwich Tern *Sterna sandvicensis.* Irregular passage migrant: almost annual.
‡ Roseate Tern *Sterna dougallii.* The only record was in 1969.
† Common Tern *Sterna hirundo.* Fairly common on passage, some breed: see page 49.
† Arctic Tern *Sterna paradisaea.* A regular passage migrant.
† Little Tern *Sterna albifrons.* Irregular passage migrant: almost annual.
† Black Tern *Chlidonias niger.* Regular on passage.
** White-winged Black Tern *Chlidonias leucopterus.* Only two records: 1929 and 1970.
† Guillemot *Uria aalge. The only two records were in 1882 and 1888.*
† Razorbill *Alca torda.* The single record was in 1934.
‡ Little Auk *Alle alle.* Very rare storm-driven vagrant, most recently in 1965 and 1967.
† Puffin *Fratercula arctica.* Very rare, generally storm-driven, last recorded 1961 and 1979.
** Pallas's Sandgrouse *Syrrhaptes paradoxus. Recorded in irruption years: 1863,1888 and 1908.*
　Feral Pigeon *Columba livia.* Widespread resident in towns: not mapped.
　Stock Dove *Columba oenas.* Common throughout the year: see page 50.
　Woodpigeon *Columba palumbus.* Common: see page 50.
　Collared Dove *Streptopelia decaocto.* Common: see page 51.
* Turtle Dove *Streptopelia turtur.* Common summer visitor: see page 52.
† Ring-necked Parakeet *Psittacula krameri.* Feral birds recorded since 1976.
* Cuckoo *Cuculus canorus.* Widespread summer visitor and on passage: see page 53.
† Barn Owl *Tyto alba.* Sparsely distributed resident: see page 54.
† Little Owl *Athene noctua.* Widespread resident: see page 55.

† Tawny Owl *Strix aluco*. Common resident: see page 56.
† Long-eared Owl *Asio otus*. Sparse resident and winter visitor: see page 57.
† Short-eared Owl *Asio flammeus*. Regular in autumn and winter: 79 best recent year.
† Nightjar *Caprimulgus europaeus*. Decreasing summer visitor: see page 58.
Swift *Apus apus*. Common summer visitor and passage migrant: see page 59.
** Alpine Swift *Apus melba*. Only two records: 1965 and 1977.
* Kingfisher *Alcedo atthis*. Widespread resident, some passage records: see page 60.
** Bee-eater *Merops apiaster*. Four records: ca.1882,1905,1955 and 1973.
** Roller *Coracias garrulus*. Only two records: 1852 and 1932.
‡ Hoopoe *Upupa epops*. Uncommon visitor: 70(2),71,73,75,76,77(2),78(4).
† Wryneck *Jynx torquilla*. Summer migrant, sporadic breeding but regular on passage: see page 61.
* Green Woodpecker *Picus viridis*. Widespread resident: see page 62.
* Great Spotted Woodpecker *Dendrocopos major*. Widespread resident: see page 63.
* Lesser Spotted Woodpecker *Dendrocopos minor*. Widespread resident: see page 63.
** White-winged Lark *Melanocorypha leucoptera*. The only record was in 1955.
‡ Woodlark *Lullula arborea*. Irregularly recorded, has bred: see page 64.
Skylark *Alauda arvensis*. Common: see page 65.
* Sand Martin *Riparia riparia*. Widespread on passage, local as breeder: see page 66.
Swallow *Hirundo rustica*. Common summer visitor and passage migrant: see page 67.
** Red-rumped Swallow *Hirundo daurica*. The only two records were in 1949 and 1966.
House Martin *Delichon urbica*. Common summer visitor: see page 67.
* Tree Pipit *Anthus trivialis*. Widespread summer visitor: see page 68.
* Meadow Pipit *Anthus pratensis*. Common winter and passage, sparse breeder: see page 69.
† Rock/Water Pipit *Anthus spinoletta*. Regular on passage and in winter (mostly *A. s. spinoletta*).
* Yellow Wagtail *Motacilla flava*. Common on passage, local breeder: see page 70.
* Grey Wagtail *Motacilla cinerea*. Common in winter, local breeder: see page 70.
Pied Wagtail *Motacilla alba*. Widespread breeder, augmented in winter: see page 71.
‡ Waxwing *Bombycilla garrulus*. Regularly seen in irruption years.
‡ Dipper *Cinclus cinclus*. Bred once ca.1910, now rare winter visitor (probably mostly Black-bellied *C. c. cinclus*): last wintered 74-75.
Wren *Troglodytes troglodytes*. Abundant resident: see page 72.
Dunnock *Prunella modularis*. Common resident: see page 73.
Robin *Erithacus rubecula*. Common resident: see page 74.
† Nightingale *Luscinia megarhynchos*. Rare and declining summer visitor: see page 75.
‡ Bluethroat *Luscinia svecica*. Only four records: 1942,1969,1970 and 1978.
† Black Redstart *Phoenicurus ochruros*. Rare passage,winter and breeding: see page 76.
† Redstart *Phoenicurus phoenicurus*. Passage migrant and local summer visitor: see page 76.
† Whinchat *Saxicola rubetra*. Passage migrant and rare summer visitor: see page 77.
† Stonechat *Saxicola torquata*. Regular in winter, very rare breeder: see page 78.
† Wheatear *Oenanthe oenanthe*. Common on passage now very rarely breeds: see page 78.
** Rock Thrush *Monticola saxatilis*. *The only record was in 1843*.
† Ring Ouzel *Turdus torquatus*. Bred once (1864): regular on passage.
Blackbird *Turdus merula*. Abundant resident and winter visitor: see page 79.
* Fieldfare *Turdus pilaris*. Common winter visitor and passage migrant.
Song Thrush *Turdus philomelos*. Abundant resident: see page 80.

118

* Redwing *Turdus iliacus*. Common winter visitor and passage migrant.
Mistle Thrush *Turdus viscivorus*. Common resident: see page 81.
† Cetti's Warbler *Cettia cetti*. First record 1975: now sparse breeding resident.
† Grasshopper Warbler *Locustella naevia*. Widespread summer visitor: see page 82.
‡ Savi's Warbler *Locustella luscinioides*. A single record in 1979.
** Aquatic Warbler *Acrocephalus paludicola*. Only recorded once: 1960.
* Sedge Warbler *Acrocephalus schoenobaenus*. Widespread summer visitor and passage migrant: see page 82.
‡ Marsh Warbler *Acrocephalus palustris*. Very rare summer vagrant: 78.
* Reed Warbler *Acrocephalus scirpaceus*. Local summer visitor (and passage): see page 83.
** Great Reed Warbler *Acrocephalus arundinaceus*. The only record was in 1946.
‡ Melodious Warbler *Hippolais polyglotta*. Only two records: 1961 and 1971.
‡ Dartford Warbler *Sylvia undata*. Eight records but none since 1947.
‡ Barred Warbler *Sylvia nisoria*. The only two records were in 1972 and 1975.
* Lesser Whitethroat *Sylvia curruca*. Summer visitor and passage migrant: see page 84.
* Whitethroat *Sylvia communis*. Summer visitor and passage migrant: see page 85.
* Garden Warbler *Sylvia borin*. Summer visitor and passage migrant: see page 86.
* Blackcap *Sylvia atricapilla*. Summer visitor, passage migrant and a few winter: see page 87.
† Wood Warbler *Phylloscopus sibilatrix*. Local summer visitor: see page 88.
Chiffchaff *Phylloscopus collybita*. Summer visitor, common passage migrant, very rare in winter: see page 89.
Willow Warbler *Phylloscopus trochilus*. Common in summer and on passage: see page 89.
* Goldcrest *Regulus regulus*. Widespread resident and winter visitor: see page 90.
‡ Firecrest *Regulus ignicapillus*. Passage migrant and winter visitor, some summer records: see page 90.
* Spotted Flycatcher *Muscicapa striata*. Summer visitor and passage migrant: see page 91.
† Pied Flycatcher *Ficedula hypoleuca*. Uncommon passage migrant.
† Bearded Tit *Panurus biarmicus*. Winter visitor in reedbeds, bred once: see page 91.
Long-tailed Tit *Aegithalos caudatus*. Common resident: see page 92.
* Marsh Tit *Parus palustris*. Widespread resident: see page 93.
* Willow Tit *Parus montanus*. Widespread resident: see page 93.
Coal Tit *Parus ater*. Common resident: see page 94.
Blue Tit *Parus caeruleus*. Abundant resident: see page 95.
Great Tit *Parus major*. Abundant resident: see page 95.
* Nuthatch *Sitta europaea*. Local resident in woodland: see page 96.
* Treecreeper *Certhia familiaris*. Widespread resident: see page 97.
‡ Golden Oriole *Oriolus oriolus*. Very rare on passage, has bred: see page 96.
† Red-backed Shrike *Lanius collurio*. Formerly widespread summer visitor, now rare on passage and even rarer breeding: see page 97.
† Great Grey Shrike *Lanius excubitor*. Regular on passage and in winter: 5-10 annually.
** Woodchat Shrike *Lanius senator*. *The only two records were in the mid-1800's*.
Jay *Garrulus glandarius*. Common in wooded areas: see page 98.
Magpie *Pica pica*. Common resident: see page 99.
** Nutcracker *Nucifraga caryocatactes*. Ten records, all in the invasion year of 1968.
Jackdaw *Corvus monedula*. Common resident: see page 99.

Rook *Corvus frugilegus.* Common resident: see page 100.

Crow *Corvus corone.* Common resident (Hooded recorded some winters): see page 101.

‡ Raven *Corvus corax.* Formerly bred, only records since 1950 in 1955 and 1968.

Starling *Sturnus vulgaris.* Abundant resident and winter visitor: see page 102.

★★ Rose-coloured Starling *Sturnus roseus.* Only three records: 1855, 1952 and 1956.

House Sparrow *Passer domesticus.* Abundant resident: see page 102.

Tree Sparrow *Passer montanus.* Common resident: see page 103.

Chaffinch *Fringilla coelebs.* Common resident and winter visitor: see page 104.

★ Brambling *Fringilla montifringilla.* Regular winter visitor and passage migrant.

★★ Serin *Serinus serinus.* The only record was in 1973.

Greenfinch *Carduelis chloris.* Very common resident: see page 104.

Goldfinch *Carduelis carduelis.* Common resident, passage and summer visitor: see page 105.

† Siskin *Carduelis spinus.* Regular passage and winter, very rare in summer: see page 106.

Linnet *Carduelis cannabina.* Common resident: see page 106.

‡ Twite *Carduelis flavirostris.* Irregular in winter: 72,74(2),77(2),78,79(3).

★ Redpoll *Carduelis flammea.* Locally common throughout the year: see page 107.

★★ Two-barred Crossbill *Loxia leucoptera.* Three records only: 1890, 1963 and 1966.

† Common Crossbill *Loxia curvirostra.* Regular during irruptions, some may stay to breed; populations may build up in conifers: see page 108.

Bullfinch *Pyrrhula pyrrhula.* Common resident: see page 108.

† Hawfinch *Coccothraustes coccothraustes.* Widespread but local resident: see page 109.

‡ Snow Bunting *Plectrophenax nivalis.* Rare winter visitor: 72(2),74,78,79.

Yellowhammer *Emberiza citrinella.* Common resident: see page 110.

‡ Cirl Bunting *Emberiza cirlus.* Formerly scarce resident, only two records in 1970's: 72,77: see page 111.

‡ Ortolan Bunting *Emberiza hortulana.* Only once recorded, in 1953.

★★ Rustic Bunting *Emberiza rustica. Only one record in 1882.*

★★ Little Bunting *Emberiza pusilla.* A single record during 1960.

Reed Bunting *Emberiza schoeniclus.* Common resident and on passage: see page 112.

Corn Bunting *Miliaria calandra.* Locally common resident: see page 113.

The Atlas maps show the distribution of each species during the breeding season. This section discusses the composite picture which they present of the overall number of species recorded in each tetrad — the *species richness*. This will depend on the types and extent of the habitats available within the four square kilometres of the tetrad and, of course, on the efforts and efficiency of the observers in finding all the species present. Figure 6.1 shows a plot of the species richness, tetrad by tetrad, with every species recorded, whether possibly, probably or proved breeding, counting towards the total. Fourteen tetrads had 76 or more species recorded in them, the black squares on the map. The maximum number, 86, was from Maple Cross (TQ09 G) with Marsworth, Tring only one behind (SP91 G). The comparison of the 14 top tetrads with the maps in chapters 2 and 3 is revealing. None were without some water — a river, stream, canal, lake or wet gravel pit — and most were in areas of mixed farming. All were basically rural but several contained only small areas of woodland — this seemed to be enough, in most cases, for almost all the woodland species to be present since there were generally major areas of woodland within a few kilometres.

The average number of species found in each of the 504 Hertfordshire tetrads was almost 52. This compares favourably with the 45 and 48 found in each London and Bedfordshire tetrad respectively. The totals for each tetrad are shown in figure 6.2, again all species recorded, whether column 1, 2 or 3, are counted. In general the tetrads in the more developed south of the county have smaller than average totals. This region includes the homes of many of the observers and was certainly well covered. The restricted species list is almost certainly a result of the urbanisation, a conclusion supported by the London Atlas figures. In the Inner City areas the average was 22 species, with 44 in outer suburbia — which includes

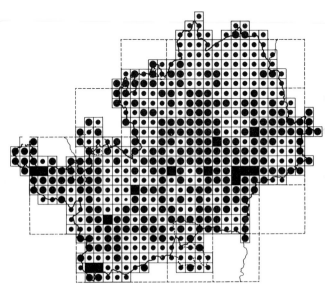

6.1 SPECIES RICH-NESS

On this map each dot shows the number of species recorded in each tetrad during the Atlas:

■ 76 or more (14 tetrads)
● 51 — 75 (259 tetrads)
● 26 — 50 (230 tetrads)
· 24 (one tetrad)

The six tetrads with more than 80 species were SP91 B & G, TQ09 G & L, TL31 R and TL32 V.

6.2 NUMBER OF SPECIES IN EACH TETRAD

This map shows the number of species recorded in each tetrad and entered as possibly, probably or proved breeding.

```
                                  37
                     30 35              40 32
                  48 35 37 40        42 51 55 44 39
                  41 39 42 50 27 36 41 43 42 44
                  48 36 38 31 25 38 44 39 40 37 34
               54 42 38 59 45 28 26 38 45 39 42 45 50 40
         46 54 50 54 46 59 52 34 33 63 52 47 36 33 39 54 51 34
         56 61 71 66 64 34 50 59 35 40 64 53 48 41 40 34 33 40 42
         63 56 50 39 47 51 56 44 59 64 55 32 34 42 50 55 47 49 48
         57 44 56 45 48 48 55 48 55 68 57 55 58 30 52 52 46 53 50 40
         38 36 55 53 50 47 50 55 56 60 50 47 31 56 65 44 56 57 40        59
   57 30       51 46 46 50 63 56 67 57 52 65 66 46 35 47 70 54 52 51 60 61 57
   56 45 52    55 38 40 62 59 63 53 65 68 65 47 41 59 82 52 58 65 57 68 70 70
48 55    62 41 41 43 59    65 42 44 58 60 50 60 53 52 78 69 51 48 68 51 57 45 39 63
54 57 53    71 31 52 45 48 64 45 52 53 49 60 57 60 69 71 61 54 59 53 55 46 42 42 53
53 58 53 45 53    70 59 66 65 49 52 36 48 53 57 58 59 58 74 66 59 66 55 63 74 70 58 39 44 43 51 65
54 81 85 64 63 60 51 61 61 47 39 44 51 49 51 62 78 71 42 65 77 70 68 76 83 78 58 53 73 73 55
64 59 55 60 67 60 62 64 42 30 50 44 46 48 69 40 60 46 39 61 68 60 77 58 75 59 38 46
54 67 68 57 46 54 52 51 47 48 27 77 56 55 61 43 47 64 59 54 42 64 66 64 66
   47 41 51 38 38 57 41 34 50 24 71 35 44 63 47 58 47 61 46 44 59 63 74
         37 38 57 60 47 50 60 53 52 47 57 64 46 50 68 64 56 54 31 52
         34 40 51 59 76 61 61 50 53 59 47 60 58 62 63 64 60 40 41 75
         40 44 37 59 67 61 51 61 53 64 60 46 61 50 68 62 63 31 27 60
         66 74 46 54 57 29 41 38 60 59 46 45 59 48           60
         73 73 56 72 31 27 43 37 31 31 34 41 67
         68 43 42 49 63 35 34 44 45 41 39 38 47 35 43
         44 86 84 44 35 47 36 53        38 52 35 40
         68 57 33 35 45
```

much of southern Hertfordshire — and 52 for rural London. In the northeast of the county, on the Boulder Clay and Chalk, the species totals were also low. These areas are farmed very intensively with little variation in habitat — large cereal fields with sparse hedges and very little standing water — and thus breeding bird communities are restricted. However it must also be said that this is probably the area with the poorest observer coverage — many tetrads had to be covered by birdwatchers living far away. They would, of course, tend to make their visits at the time of year when the greatest variety of species could be recorded and may have missed species best found early or late in the season. However the same conditions — large arable fields, little woodland or standing water — also coincided with other areas showing a restricted range of species. Examples include the region between Hemel Hempstead and Harpenden, the central part of TL41 and the area on the borders of SP90 and TL00. In all three areas few tetrads reach the 50 species mark and many were near 40. However, only a few kilometres away, where the habitat is more varied the scores regularly exceed 60 species. Comparison with the arable map (figure 3.1) shows that, in general, the highly arable areas are relatively poor in bird species.

In one square (TL10 D) only 24 species were recorded. Almost the whole of this tetrad lies within the bounds of one private estate from which, through a misunderstanding, the local fieldworker was excluded although permission to enter had been granted to the organisers. Otherwise there were very few problems

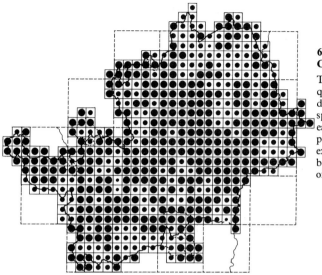

in obtaining permission to visit private areas throughout the county. A very few sensitive places, such as a firework factory, some explosive stores and petroleum installations remained 'out of bounds' but this will not have had a significant effect as the habitats that they represented were accessible elsewhere in each tetrad.

The question of the quality of coverage is crucial — any atlas that purports to show the distribution of breeding species must be the outcome of good and uniform coverage. In Hertfordshire we were fortunate in being able to mobilise a large and enthusiastic band of volunteers to carry out the fieldwork — over 250 are named in the acknowledgements and many others, unknown to us by name also helped. To ensure as uniform cover as possible the observers were directed to tetrads from which it was judged that extra records were needed. These were discovered by comparing the number of species recorded with an assessment, made when the fieldwork was starting, of the number of species to be expected in each tetrad. This was based on a thorough examination of the 1 : 25 000 Ordnance Survey maps and a subjective scoring of species according to the available habitats. Each was therefore simply a number (actually multiples of five) and not, in any sense, a made-up species list — in any case the fieldworkers were never shown the results of the assessments. What did happen, for the last two years of the survey, was that the observers were told which tetrads were seriously under-recorded and were asked to direct their efforts there. Figure 3.3 shows, as a dot map, the final percentage of species found of the totals assessed. On average 86% was achieved and two thirds of the tetrads had 80% or better. In a handful of embarrassing cases 100% was exceeded but mostly there had been a gross alteration in the habitats available since the maps had been published — for example new gravel diggings. The minimum for any tetrad was 40% (TL10 D again) but there were only two others with less than 50% of the assessed number of species. We are confident that the coverage achieved was not only very good but also uniform.

ACKNOWLEDGEMENTS

A book like this relies on the help of hundreds of people but we feel we must single out a few. Jim Flegg and Chris Cox were joint organisers before they returned to their native Kent. A succession of county recorders were very helpful and Tom Gladwin provided us with statistics about the county. Tim Sharrock encouraged us throughout and wrote the foreword. The B.T.O. provided both advice from the staff and also the data for us to calculate the local C.B.C. indices — in themselves the result of thousands of hours of fieldwork. We received much help, pre-publication, from John Dony, Trevor Poyser and Keith Maund. We have also managed to produce the book in our 'spare time' without antagonising our wives, Linda and Verity, *too* much! However our chief debt of gratitude is to the observers who contributed the records. All those we have been able to trace are named below. Our apologies to those we have omitted but many records were submitted in the name of local groups or societies and we cannot know who helped to gather them. Thank you one and all.

N. Agar, M. J. Allen, J. Arkell, D. J. Armitage, R. S. Bailey, C. Bains, J. K. Baker, D. Ball, E. W. Balmer, R. Barker, M. J. Barrett, Mrs. E. Barron, B. Barton, Mrs. S. Barton, L. A. Batten, M. Bavin, J. Baynton, D. H. Beal, A. J. Beard, T. G. Beynon, C. J. Bibby, Bishop's Stortford Natural History Society, M. J. Blindell, R. M. Blindell, D. F. Bowman, R. Bradbrook, C. Brown, A. Broxup, C. W. Burton, G. Buss, D. Cantrill, R. P. Chainey, D. K. Chesterman, A. R. Child, C. S. Clapham, K. C. Clarke, P. Coleman, A. Collin, A. Collis, P. Collis, Miss J. E. Compton, J. A. Cooper, Miss C. M. Cousins, Mrs. S. Cowdy, C. J. Cox, D. A. H. Crawford, J. E. Crawford, Mrs. E. Crawford, S. E. Crooks, N. Cross, J. C. Crudass, A. Cudmore, Mrs. E. H. Cunningham, Miss J. M. Currell, R. B. Curtis, P. Daltrey, G. L. Daltrey, N. Davidson, Mrs. I. J. Davis, J. C. H. Day, P. Delaloye, D. Denham, T. R. E. Devlin, R. E. Dimsdale, J. G. Dony, K. Douver, J. P. Dowsett, K. Dugmore, W. W. Dunn, J. N. Dymond, P. Earl, J. C. Eaton, R. Edwards, M. C. Elliott, D. Ellis, M. Endean, T. J. Ennis, D. W. Evans, J. D. Fearnside, A. Fisher, M. Fitch, T. J. M. Flegg, H. Franklin, Miss J. Franklin, R. J. Fuller, J. Galton, N. T. Gammon, I. C. Gardner, R. W. George, P. W. Gerrard, H. B. Ginn, Mrs. J. M. Gladwin, T. W. Gladwin, J. Glen, D. E. Glue, A. E. Goodall, Miss J. Greenfield, C. Gregory, Miss P. D. Hager, K. J. Hall, R. Hamilton, R. Harding, R. A. Hardinge, E. W. Hawken, J. Herring, Mrs. Hinchcliffe, R. A. Hoblyn, M. Y. Holdsworth, D. T. Holyoak, A. Horder, I. M. Horn, R. Hudson, H. E. Hutson, M. P. Ingram, J. Jack, A. C. Jackson, P. Jackson, T. James, A. R. Jenkins, I. G. Johnson, J. J. Johnson, A. Jones, K. R. Jones, N. R. Jones, M. July, Miss D. Keating, A. S. Keith, C. R. Kightley, J. R. J. King, Mrs. J. H. King, W. H. C. Kingham, P. A. Kingsbury, T. Kittle, P. U. le Neve Foster, Miss V. M. Leather, A. B. Lees, D. D. Lees, R. Leighton, Miss M. Levy, Miss E. A. Linsell, S. E. Linsell, A. J. Livett, London Natural History Society, R. L. Longland, P. A. MacKenzie Dyer, J. D. Magee, Maple Cross Ringing Station, D. Marsland, M. Mathias, D. J. Matthews, Miss E. Maughan, H. Mayer-Gross, C. J. Mead, Mrs. U. V. Mead, B. S. Meadows, J. Melling, Merchant Taylor's School Field Club, G. S. Moffat, P. W. Moles, G. J. Moore, E. S. Morris, S. Morris, A. C. Morriss, E. J. Moynahan, B. S. Nau, D. W. Newell, A. Noble, R. B. Norden, E. C. Offord, Mrs. A. Offord, E. C. Ormerod, R. Palmer, L. E. Parr, R. J. Peacock, J. N. Porter, A. J. Prater, Mrs. A. C. Pratt, J. M. Purdey, M. A. Pyle, R.S.P.B. Local Groups, L. A. Rance, R. E. Rayment, T. J. Revill, A. Reynolds, Mrs. J. H. Ring, C. Rose, R. W. Roseveare, Rye Meads Ringing Group, B. L. Sage, D. I. Sales, R. F. Sanderson, B. R. Sawford, J. Sculpham, H. B. Secretan, P. J. Sellar, J. T. R. Sharrock, B. Sillis, J. Simon, A. F. Slatter, H. A. Slatter, H. E. Smyth, D. W. Snow, Mrs. B. Snow, T. Spall, Mrs. M. A. Spencer, R. Spencer, B. Squires, P. Stapleton, Stevenage Ornithological Society, A. D. Stock, T. W. Stokes, W. A. Stokes, B. Sutton, P. Tate, J. H. Terry, R. J. Thatcher, M. E. Tibbett, C. T. W. Tipper, R. J. Tomlin, Mrs. Topham, M. Tout, P. Trodd, Miss B. Turner, C. D. H. Vernon, P. Walton, E. H. Warmington, M. Warren, Mrs. Warren, Welwyn Natural History Society, D. W. West, R. Weyl, A. F. White, A. Whittall, P. Whittall, G. F. Whitwell, J. P. Widgery, R. P. Widgery, L. K. Wilkinson, P. J. Wilkinson, K. Williamson, R. J. Wilmshurst, D. R. Wilson, J. Wilson, D. Wood, G. Wood, Mrs. R. P. Woods, R. P. Woods, W. L. Woods, W. J. Young.

BIBLIOGRAPHY

Dony, J. G. (1967) *Flora of Hertfordshire*. Hitchin Museum.
Gardner, H. W. (1967) *A Survey of the Agriculture of Hertfordshire*. Royal Agricultural Society of England, London.
Hinton, R. F. (1980) *A Survey of Ancient, Semi-natural Woodland in Hertfordshire*. H.M.T.N.C., Offley.
James, T. J. (1981) The Distribution and Ecology of the Wood Warbler in Hertfordshire. *Trans.H.N.H.S.*, **28, Pt.5:** 24-29.
Perring, F. H. & S. M. Walters. (1962) *Atlas of the British Flora*. Nelson, London.
Sage, B. L. (1959) *A History of the Birds of Hertfordshire*. Barrie & Rockliff, London.
Sage, B. L. (1980) The Species of Birds Recorded in Hertfordshire. *Trans.H.N.H.S.*, **28, Pt. 3:** 45-56.
Sawford, B. R. (1981) 1980 Nightingale Survey: Hertfordshire Results. *Trans.H.N.H.S.*, **28, Pt.5:** 30-32.
Voous, K. H. (1977) *List of Recent Holarctic Bird Species*. Academic Press, London.

THE BIRD ATLASES

These Bird Atlases are listed in the order in which they are quoted under each species. If you find it difficult to order them through your local bookseller then those still in print are obtainable through the Scottish Ornithologist's Club Bird Bookshop, 21 Regent Terrace, Edinburgh EH7 5BT. The National Atlas is, of course, available direct from the B.T.O. (Beech Grove, Tring, Herts HP23 5NR).

BEDFORDSHIRE *Bedfordshire Bird Atlas*. B. D. Harding (1979) Bedfordshire Natural History Society, Bedford.
LONDON *Atlas of the Breeding Birds of the London Area*. D. J. Montier (1977) Batsford, London.
KENT *The Birds of Kent*. D. W. Taylor, D. L. Davenport & J. J. M. Flegg (1981) Kent Ornithological Society.*
GREAT BRITAIN AND IRELAND *The Atlas of the Breeding Birds in Britain and Ireland*. J. T. R. Sharrock (1976) T. & A. D. Poyser, Calton.
FRANCE *Atlas des Oiseaux Nicheurs de France*. L. Yeatman (1976) Ministère de la Qualité de la Vie Environnement, Paris.
BRITTANY Histoire et Geographie des Oiseaux Nicheurs de Bretagne. Y. Guermeur & J-Y. Monnat (1980) *Ar Vran*, 8.
NETHERLANDS *Atlas van de Nederlandse Broedvogels*. R. M. Teixeira (1979) Vereniging tot Behoud van Natuurmonumenten in Nederland.

Further National Atlases have been published in Europe (Denmark and Switzerland) or are in the course of being prepared.

* Unlike the other Atlases the Kent work is also a complete history of the county's birds throughout the year.

NATIONAL AND LOCAL ORGANISATIONS

BRITISH TRUST FOR ORNITHOLOGY, Beech Grove, Tring, Herts HP23 5NR. The B.T.O. is the national organisation for active ornithologists interested in making a contribution to our knowledge of birds. This is achieved through the permanent enquiries: Bird Ringing, Common Birds Census, Nest Record Scheme and Waterways Bird Survey as well as through special projects like the National Atlas of Breeding Birds, the Winter Atlas and the Birds of Estuaries Enquiry. Members receive a journal *Bird Study*, a newsletter *BTO News* and may attend conferences, courses and meetings held in various parts of the country. The B.T.O. also publishes various field guides and lists. Write to Beech Grove for full membership details.

ROYAL SOCIETY FOR THE PROTECTION OF BIRDS, The Lodge, Sandy, Beds. SG19 2DL. All British birdwatchers should be members of the R.S.P.B., Europe's largest voluntary wildlife conservation body with over 340 000 members. Its activities include the acquisition and management of reserves throughout the country, the arrangement of special protection schemes for rare breeding birds and the investigation of offences against protection laws. Anyone suspecting that these laws may have been broken should phone the investigations department on Sandy 80551. Young birdwatchers are catered for through the **YOUNG ORNITHOLOGISTS' CLUB.** Apart from national meetings there are many local film shows and most parts of the country are served by local members' groups which have evening meetings and field outings. Such groups in Hertfordshire are currently based on Chorleywood, Harpenden, Hemel Hempstead, Hertford, Hitchin, Potters Bar, St. Albans, Southeast Herts (Lea Valley), Watford and Welwyn Garden City. Full details are available from The Lodge.

BRITISH BIRDS, Fountains, Park Lane, Blunham, Beds MK44 3NJ. A recently independent monthly journal published continuously since 1909; BB is something of an institution amongst birders. Apart from scientific papers of high quality regular features include 'Recent Reports' and a mystery photograph quiz. A sample issue and details of subscription rates will be sent on request.

ROYAL SOCIETY FOR NATURE CONSERVATION, The Green, Nettleham, Lincoln LN2 2NR. The R.S.N.C. (formerly the Society for the Promotion of Nature Reserves) is the umbrella organisation under which the County Naturalist's Trust movement is co-ordinated. All individual members of the 42 County Trusts are associate members of the R.S.N.C. and you may obtain membership details of all these trusts by contacting the office at Nettleham.

ROYAL SOCIETY FOR THE PREVENTION OF CRUELTY TO ANIMALS. The R.S.P.C.A. is not an organisation to which birders generally belong but it does offer a service to everyone which may be of very great help. Its national system of inspectors (see phone book for details) will always try to help anybody with an injured bird or animal.

HERTFORDSHIRE NATURAL HISTORY SOCIETY. The Society organises indoor and field meetings on a wide variety of topics — the Ornithological Section has a reduced subscription fee for those not wishing to join in other activities. Close contact is kept both with the B.T.O. and with the county's local societies (see below). The County Bird Report is compiled by the Recorder: Bruce Taggart, 60 Pruden Close, Mayfield Avenue, Southgate, London N14. To ease his burden records should be submitted each half year in July and January. Back numbers of the Report and details of membership of the H.N.H.S. and the Ornithological Section may be obtained from Philip Kingsbury, 6 Castle Hill, Berkhamsted.

Local Societies within the County:
Bishop's Stortford and District N.H.S. Margaret Lewis, 30 Kings Court, Bishop's Stortford.
Letchworth Naturalists' Society c/o North Herts Museums, Old Fire Station, High Street, Baldock.
Stevenage Bird Watching Society Peter Walton, Twin Oaks, Rabley Heath, Welwyn.
Welwyn Natural History Society Tom Kittle, 36 Newtown, Codicote, Hitchin.
Lea Valley Project Group Kevin Roberts, 32 Caxton Road, Hoddesdon.

Societies in adjacent counties:
Buckinghamshire Bird Club Jim Knight, 319 Bath Road, Cippenham, Slough. Jim is county recorder. The organiser of their current tetrad atlas project is Trevor Brooks, 8 Coombe Crescent, Thame, Oxon.
Bedfordshire N.H.S. Mrs. M. Sheridan, 28 Chestnut Hill, Linslade, Leighton Buzzard. The recorder is Barry Nightingale, 9 Duck End Lane, Maulden, Beds.
Cambridge Bird Club Bruce S. Martin, 178 Nuns Way, Cambridge CB4 2NS. The recorder is C. A. E. Kirtland, 22 Montgomerey Road, Cambridge CB4 2EQ.
Essex B.W.P.S. Mrs. J. Sunnuck, 183 Priest's Lane, Shenfield CM15 8LF. The recorder is J. Howard, 6 St. Bride Court, Colchester CO4 4PQ.
London N.H.S. (Ornithological Section) Mrs. O. L. Cassie, 15 Kingsway, Town Lane, Stanwell, Middlesex.

The Naturalists' Trusts:
Hertfordshire and Middlesex Trust for Nature Conservation Grebe House, St Michaels Street, St Albans, Herts. All who are interested in the local countryside should be members of the H.M.T.N.C. as the local organisation which manages reserves both purchased outright and through agreements with owners. Several new areas are added each year and help is always needed both with fund-raising and practical work on the reserves.
Berkshire, Buckinghamshire and Oxfordshire Naturalists' Trust. R. C. S. Lowe (Hon. Sec.), 122 Church Way, Iffley, Oxford OX4 4EG.
Bedfordshire and Huntingdonshire Naturalists' Trust Dr. N. Dawson, 38 Mill Street, Bedford MK40 3HD.
Cambridge and Isle of Ely Naturalists' Trust K. McNaught, 1 Brookside, Cambridge CB2 1JF.
Essex Naturalists' Trust Sqn. Ldr. P. G. Murton, Fingringhoe Wick Nature Reserve, South Green Road, Fingringhoe, Colchester CO5 7DN.

INDEX

Page references are given to the main account for each species and bold type is used for the large version of each habitat map.